Britisl

LOC

FIFTY-SIXTH EDITION
2014

The complete guide to all
Locomotives which operate on
the national railway network
and Eurotunnel

Robert Pritchard & Peter Hall

ISBN 978 1909 431 05 8

© 2013. Platform 5 Publishing Ltd, 3 Wyvern House, Sark Road, Sheffield,
S2 4HG, England.

Printed in England by Berforts Information Press, Eynsham, Oxford.

CONTENTS

PROVISION OF INFORMATION

This book has been compiled with care to be as accurate as possible, but in some cases information is not officially available and the publisher cannot be held responsible for any errors or omissions. We would like to thank the companies and individuals which have been co-operative in supplying information to us. The authors of this series of books are always pleased to receive notification from readers of any inaccuracies readers may find in the series, to enhance future editions. Please send comments to:

Robert Pritchard, Platform 5 Publishing Ltd, 3 Wyvern House, Sark Road, Sheffield, S2 4HG, England.

e-mail: robert@platform5.com   **Tel:** 0114 255 2625   **Fax:** 0114 255 2471.

This book is updated to information received by 7 October 2013.

UPDATES

This book is updated to the Stock Changes given in **Today's Railways UK 143** (November 2013). Readers are therefore advised to update this book from the official Platform 5 Stock Changes published every month in **Today's Railways UK** magazine, starting with issue 144.

The Platform 5 magazine **Today's Railways UK** contains news and rolling stock information on the railways of Britain and Ireland and is published on the second Monday of every month. For further details of **Today's Railways UK**, please see the advertisement on the back cover of this book.

Front cover photograph: Freightliner 70017, with 70018 behind dead-in-train, hauls 4O51 09.58 Wentloog–Southampton intermodal through Undy, between Cardiff and Newport on 10/07/13.   **Ron Westwater**

BRITAIN'S RAILWAY SYSTEM

INFRASTRUCTURE & OPERATION

Britain's national railway infrastructure is owned by a "not for dividend" company, Network Rail (NR). Many stations and maintenance depots are leased to and operated by Train Operating Companies (TOCs), but some larger stations remain under NR control. The only exception is the infrastructure on the Isle of Wight, which is nationally owned and leased to South West Trains.

Trains are operated by TOCs over Network Rail, regulated by access agreements between the parties involved. In general, TOCs are responsible for the provision and maintenance of the locomotives, rolling stock and staff necessary for the direct operation of services, whilst NR is responsible for the provision and maintenance of the infrastructure and also for staff to regulate the operation of services.

During 2012 the letting of new franchises was suspended pending a review of the franchise system following the cancelling of the award of the West Coast franchise to First Group. The process was restarted in 2013 but it is going to take a number of years to catch-up and several franchises are to receive short-term extensions in the meantime. At the time of writing extensions had been agreed with First for First Capital Connect and Great Western, whilst Invitations to Tender had been issued for two new franchises – Essex Thameside and the combined Thameslink, Southern & Great Northern franchise.

DOMESTIC PASSENGER TRAIN OPERATORS

The large majority of passenger trains are operated by the TOCs on fixed-term franchises. Franchise expiry dates are shown in the list of franchisees below:

Franchise	Franchisee	Trading Name
Chiltern	Deutsche Bahn (Arriva) (until 31 December 2021)	**Chiltern Railways**

Chiltern Railways operates a frequent service between London Marylebone, Banbury and Birmingham Snow Hill, with some peak trains extending to Kidderminster. There are also regular services from Marylebone to Stratford-upon-Avon and to Aylesbury Vale Parkway via Amersham (along the London Underground Metropolitan Line). The fleet consists of DMUs of Classes 121 (used on the Princes Risborough–Aylesbury route), 165, 168 and 172 plus a number of loco-hauled rakes used on some of the Birmingham trains, worked by Class 67s hired from DB Schenker.

Cross-Country	Deutsche Bahn (Arriva) (until 31 March 2016)*	**CrossCountry**

Franchise extension to be negotiated to November 2019.

CrossCountry operates a network of long distance services between Scotland, North-East England and Manchester to the South-West of England, Reading, Southampton, Bournemouth and Guildford, centred on Birmingham New Street. These trains are mainly formed of diesel Class 220/221 Voyagers, supplemented by a small number of HSTs on the NE–SW route. Inter-urban services also link Nottingham, Leicester and Stansted Airport with Birmingham and Cardiff. These use Class 170 DMUs.

| **East Midlands** | Stagecoach Group plc (until 31 March 2015)* | **East Midlands Trains** |

Franchise extension to be negotiated to October 2017.

EMT operates a mix of long distance high speed services on the Midland Main Line (MML), from London St Pancras to Sheffield (Leeds at peak times and some extensions to York/Scarborough) and Nottingham, and local and regional services ranging from the Norwich–Liverpool route to Nottingham–Skegness, Nottingham–Mansfield–Worksop, Nottingham–Matlock and Derby–Crewe. It also operates local services in Lincolnshire. Trains on the MML are worked by a fleet of Class 222 DMUs and ten HSTs, whilst the local and regional fleet consists of DMU Classes 153, 156 and 158.

| **Essex Thameside** | National Express Group plc (until 13 September 2014) | **c2c** |

c2c operates an intensive, principally commuter, service from London Fenchurch Street to Southend and Shoeburyness via both Upminster and Tilbury. The fleet consists entirely of Class 357 EMUs.

Franchise may be extended to 2 May 2015 if required.

| **Greater Western** | First Group plc (until 20 September 2015) | **First Great Western** |

First Great Western operates long distance trains from London Paddington to South Wales, the West Country and Worcester and Hereford. In addition there are frequent trains along the Thames Valley corridor to Newbury and Oxford, plus local and regional trains throughout the South-West including the Cornish, Devon and Thames Valley branches, the Reading–Gatwick North Downs line and Cardiff–Portsmouth Harbour and Bristol–Weymouth regional routes. A fleet of 53 HSTs is used on the long-distance trains, with DMUs of Classes 165, 166 used on the North Downs and Thames Valley routes and Class 180s used alongside HSTs on the Cotswold Line to Worcester and Hereford. Classes 143, 150, 153 and 158 are used on local and regional trains in the South-West. A small fleet of four Class 57s is maintained to work the overnight "Cornish Riviera" Sleeper service between London and Penzance.

| **Greater Anglia** | Abellio (NS) (until 19 July 2014) | **Greater Anglia** |

Franchise extension to be negotiated to October 2016.

Greater Anglia operates main line trains between London Liverpool Street, Ipswich and Norwich and local trains across Norfolk, Suffolk and parts of Cambridgeshire. It also runs local and commuter services into Liverpool Street from the Great Eastern (including Southend, Braintree and Clacton) and West Anglia (including Cambridge and Stansted Airport) routes. It operates a very varied fleet of Class 90s with loco-hauled Mark 3 sets, DMUs of Classes 153, 156 and 170 and EMUs of Classes 315, 317, 321, 360 and 379.

| **Integrated Kent** | Govia Ltd (Go-Ahead/Keolis) (until 12 October 2014) | **Southeastern** |

Franchise extension to be negotiated to June 2018.

Southeastern operates all services in the South-East London suburbs, the whole of Kent and part of Sussex, which are primarily commuter services to London. It also operates domestic high speed trains on HS1 from St Pancras to Ashford, Ramsgate, Dover and Faversham with additional peak services on other routes. EMUs of Classes 375, 376, 465 and 466 are used, along with Class 395s on the High Speed trains.

| **InterCity East Coast** | Directly Operated Railways
(until February 2015) | **East Coast** |

Currently run on an interim basis by DfT management company Directly Operated Railways (trading as East Coast). This arrangement is due to continue until a new franchise is let to the private sector in 2015.

East Coast operates frequent long distance trains on the East Coast Main Line between London King's Cross, Leeds, York, Newcastle and Edinburgh, with less frequent services to Bradford, Harrogate, Skipton, Hull, Lincoln, Glasgow, Aberdeen and Inverness. A mixed fleet of Class 91s and 30 Mark 4 sets, and 14 HST sets, are used on these trains.

| **InterCity West Coast** | Virgin Rail Group Ltd
(until 9 November 2014) | **Virgin Trains** |

Franchise extension to be negotiated to April 2017.

Virgin operates long distance services along the West Coast Main Line from London Euston to Birmingham/Wolverhampton, Manchester, Liverpool and Glasgow using Class 390 Pendolino EMUs. It also operates Class 221 Voyagers on Euston–Chester–Holyhead, whilst a mixture of 221s and 390s are used on the Birmingham–Glasgow/Edinburgh route. One rake of Mark 3 loco-hauled stock is also leased as cover, but is only normally used for special workings.

| **London Rail** | MTR/Deutsche Bahn
(until 12 November 2016) | **London Overground** |

This is a Concession and is different from other rail franchises, as fares and service levels are set by Transport for London instead of the DfT.

London Overground operates services on the Richmond–Stratford North London Line and the Willesden Junction–Clapham Junction West London Line, plus the new East London Line from Highbury & Islington to New Cross and New Cross Gate, with extensions to Clapham Jn (via Denmark Hill), Crystal Palace and West Croydon. It also runs services from London Euston to Watford Junction. All these use Class 378 EMUs whilst Class 172 DMUs are used on the Gospel Oak–Barking route.

| **Merseyrail Electrics** | Serco/Abellio (NS)
(until 19 July 2028) | **Merseyrail** |

Under the control of Merseytravel PTE instead of the DfT. Franchise reviewed every five years to fit in with the Merseyside Local Transport Plan.

Merseyrail operates services between Liverpool and Southport, Ormskirk, Kirkby, Hunts Cross, New Brighton, West Kirby, Chester and Ellesmere Port, all worked by EMUs of Classes 507 and 508.

| **Northern Rail** | Serco/Abellio (NS)
(until 1 April 2014)* | **Northern** |

Franchise extension to be negotiated to April 2017.

Northern operates a range of inter-urban, commuter and rural services throughout the North of England, including those around the cities of Leeds, Manchester, Sheffield, Liverpool and Newcastle. The network extends from Chathill in the north to Nottingham in the south, and Cleethorpes in the east to St Bees in the west. Long distance services include Leeds–Carlisle, Middlesbrough–Carlisle, Leeds–Nottingham and York–Blackpool North. The operator uses a large fleet of DMUs of Classes 142, 144, 150, 153, 155, 156 and 158 and EMUs of Classes 321, 322, 323 and 333.

ScotRail   First Group plc   **ScotRail**
(until 31 March 2015)

ScotRail provides almost all passenger services within Scotland and also trains from Glasgow to Carlisle via Dumfries, some of which extend to Newcastle (jointly operated with Northern). The company also operates the overnight Caledonian Sleeper services between London and Glasgow, Edinburgh, Inverness, Aberdeen and Fort William. In addition to the Sleeper loco-hauled stock (hauled by Class 67s and 90s hired from DB Schenker), the company operates a large fleet of DMUs of Classes 156, 158 and 170 and EMU Classes 314, 318, 320, 334 and 380. One loco-hauled rake is also used on a Fife Circle commuter train, hauled by a Class 67.

South Central   Govia Ltd (Go-Ahead/Keolis)   **Southern**
(until 25 July 2015)*

Upon termination of the Southern franchise in July 2015 it is to be combined with the existing First Capital Connect franchise to form a new Thameslink, Southern & Great Northern franchise.

Southern operates predominantly commuter services between London, Surrey and Sussex, as well as services along the South Coast between Southampton, Brighton, Hastings and Ashford, and also the cross-London service linking South Croydon and Milton Keynes. It also operates metro services in South London and Gatwick Express, which is a premium non-stop service between London Victoria and Gatwick Airport. Class 171 DMUs are used on Brighton–Ashford and London Bridge–Uckfield services, whilst all other services are in the hands of EMUs of Classes 313, 377, 442, 455 and 456. The Class 456s are due to transfer to South West Trains in early 2014.

South Western   Stagecoach Group plc   **South West Trains**
(until 3 February 2017)*

Franchise extension to be negotiated to April 2019.

South West Trains operates trains from London Waterloo to destinations across the South and South-West including Woking, Basingstoke, Southampton, Portsmouth, Salisbury, Exeter, Reading and Weymouth as well as suburban services from Waterloo. SWT also runs services between Ryde and Shanklin on the Isle of Wight, using former London Underground 1938 stock (Class 483). The rest of the fleet consists of DMU Classes 158 and 159 and EMU Classes 444, 450, 455 and 458. The fleet of Class 456s are due to be transferred from Southern to SWT in early 2014 and the fleet of 30 4-car 458s are currently being augmented to 36 5-car units with the addition of the former Gatwick Express Class 460 units to the fleet.

Thameslink & Great Northern   First Group plc   **First Capital Connect**
(until 13 September 2014)

A new Thameslink & Great Northern franchise is planned to start in September 2014. In July 2015 this will be combined with the Southern franchise.

First Capital Connect operates trains on the Thameslink route between Bedford and Brighton via central London and also on the Sutton and Wimbledon loops. A joint service with Southeastern is also operated to Sevenoaks, Orpington and Ashford. FCC also runs services on the Great Northern route between London King's Cross and Moorgate to Welwyn Garden City, Hertford North, Peterborough, Cambridge and Kings Lynn. The fleet consists of EMU Classes 319 and 377 for the Thameslink route services and Classes 313, 317, 321 and 365 for the Great Northern route services.

| **Trans-Pennine Express** | First Group/Keolis (until 1 April 2015) | **TransPennine Express** |

Franchise extension to be negotiated to February 2016.

TransPennine Express operates predominantly long distance inter-urban services linking major cities across the North of England, along with Edinburgh and Glasgow in Scotland. The main services are Manchester Airport/Manchester Piccadilly–Newcastle/Middlesbrough/Hull plus Liverpool–Scarborough and Liverpool–Newcastle (from December 2013) along the North Trans-Pennine route via Huddersfield, Leeds and York, and Manchester Airport–Cleethorpes along the South Trans-Pennine route via Sheffield. It also operates Manchester Airport–Blackpool/Barrow/Windermere/Edinburgh/Glasgow. The fleet consists of DMU Classes 170 (used on the Hull and Cleethorpes routes) and 185. Between December 2013 and May 2014 Class 350 EMUs will be introduced onto the Manchester Airport–Scotland services.

| **Wales & Borders** | Deutsche Bahn (Arriva) (until 14 October 2018)* | **Arriva Trains Wales** |

The franchise agreement includes the provision for the term to be further extended by mutual agreement by up to five years beyond October 2018. Management of the franchise is devolved to the Welsh Government, but DfT is still the procuring authority.

Arriva Trains Wales operates a mix of long distance, regional and local services throughout Wales, including the Valley Lines network of lines around Cardiff, and also through services to the English border counties and to Manchester and Birmingham. The fleet consists of DMUs of Classes 142, 143, 150, 158 and 175 and one loco-hauled rake used on a premium Welsh Government sponsored service on the Cardiff–Holyhead route, hauled by a Class 67.

| **West Midlands** | Govia Ltd (Go-Ahead/Keolis) (until 19 September 2015)* | **London Midland** |

Franchise extension to be negotiated to June 2017.

London Midland operates long distance and regional services from London Euston to Northampton and Birmingham/Crewe and also between Birmingham and Liverpool as well as local and regional services around Birmingham, including to Stratford-upon-Avon, Worcester, Hereford, Redditch and Shrewsbury. It also operates the Bedford–Bletchley and Watford Jn–St Albans Abbey branches. The fleet consists of DMU Classes 150, 153, 170 and 172 and EMU Classes 321, 323 and 350.

* Franchise agreement includes provision for an extension of up to seven 4-week reporting periods.

The following operators run non-franchised services (* special summer services only):

Operator	Trading Name	Route
BAA	Heathrow Express	London Paddington–Heathrow Airport
First Hull Trains	First Hull Trains	London King's Cross–Hull
Grand Central	Grand Central	London King's Cross–Sunderland/ Bradford Interchange
North Yorkshire Moors Railway Enterprises	North Yorkshire Moors Railway	Pickering–Grosmont–Whitby/ Battersby
West Coast Railway Company	West Coast Railway Company	Birmingham–Stratford-upon-Avon* Fort William–Mallaig* York–Wakefield–York–Scarborough*

INTERNATIONAL PASSENGER OPERATIONS

Eurostar (UK) operates passenger services between the UK and mainland Europe, jointly with the national operators of France (SNCF) and Belgium (SNCB/NMBS). Eurostar International is owned by three shareholders: SNCF (55%), London & Continental Railways (40%) and SNCB (5%).

In addition, a service for the conveyance of accompanied road vehicles through the Channel Tunnel is provided by the tunnel operating company, Eurotunnel.

FREIGHT TRAIN OPERATIONS

The following operators operate freight services or empty passenger stock workings under "Open Access" arrangements:

Colas Rail: In addition to its On-Track Machines and infrastructure activities, Colas Rail operates a number of freight flows, principally steel traffic to Boston using its Class 56s and coal from Wolsingham to Ratcliffe plus timber from Carlisle, Ribblehead and Teignbridge to Chirk using its Class 56s or 66s. The small fleet of three Class 47s are used as required.

DB Schenker Rail (UK): Still the biggest freight operator in the country, DBS (formerly EWS before being bought by DB) has seen some of its core traffic lost to competitors in recent years. It still provides a large number of infrastructure trains to Network Rail and operates coal, steel, intermodal and aggregate trains nationwide. The core fleet is Class 66s. Of the original 250 ordered 176 are still used in the UK at the time of writing, with the remainder having moved to DB's French and Polish operations, although some of the French locos do return to the UK when major maintenance is required. A fleet of between 20 and 25 Class 60s are also used on the heavier trains, this class is currently receiving overhauls.

DBS's six Class 59/2s are used alongside the Mendip Rail 59/0s and 59/1s on stone traffic from the Mendip quarries and around the South-East. DBS's fleet of Class 67s are mainly used on passenger or standby duties for Arriva Trains Wales, Chiltern Railways, East Coast and ScotRail. Class 90s are hired to ScotRail for use on the Sleeper services but see little use on freight, whilst the fleet of Class 92s are mainly used on intermodal duties, including a limited number of overnight trains on High Speed 1.

DBS also operates a number of both steam and diesel charter trains.

Devon & Cornwall Railways (a subsidiary of British American Railway Services): DCRail mainly operates scrap and spoil trains using its fleet of 56s and also provides locos from its fleet of 31s or 56s for stock moves.

Direct Rail Services: DRS has built on its original nuclear flask traffic to operate a number of different services. The main flows are intermodal (mostly Anglo-Scottish) plus the provision of crews and locos to Network Rail for autumn Railhead Treatment Trains. Its Class 47s are also used on charter work. DRS has the most varied fleet of locomotives of all the operators, with Class 20s, 37s, 47s, 57s and 66s. It has also ordered 15 new Vossloh diesels (Class 68s) and 10 new Vossloh electric locos (Class 88s), that will also feature a diesel engine.

Freightliner: Freightliner has two divisions: Intermodal operates container trains from the main Ports at Southampton, Felixstowe, Tilbury and Thamesport to major cities including London, Manchester, Leeds and Birmingham. The Heavy Haul division covers the movement of coal, cement, infrastructure and aggregates nationwide. Most services are worked by Class 66s, with new Class 70s used on some of the heavier intermodal trains and some Heavy Haul flows, principally coal, cement and Network Rail ballast trains. A small fleet of Class 86 and 90 electrics is used on intermodal trains on the Great Eastern and West Coast Main Lines, the Class 86s mainly being used in pairs on the WCML between Crewe and Coatbridge.

GB Railfreight: GBRf, owned by Eurotunnel, operates a mixture of traffic types, mainly using Class 66s together with a small fleet of Class 73s on infrastructure duties in the South-East. A growing fleet of Class 92s is also used on some intermodal flows to/from Dollands Moor and on an Ipswich–Trafford Park train. Traffic includes coal, intermodal, biomass and gypsum as well as infrastructure services for Network Rail and London Underground.

West Coast Railway Company: WCRC has a freight licence but doesn't operate any freight as such – only empty stock movements. Its fleet of 47s, supplemented by a smaller number of 33s, 37s and 57s, is used on charter work nationwide, including the prestigious Royal Scotsman.

MAINTENANCE OF LOCOMOTIVES

Depot allocation codes for all locomotives are shown in this book (apart from shunters where the actual location of each is shown). It should be noted that today much locomotive maintenance is undertaken away from these depots. This may be undertaken at fuelling points, berthing sidings or similar, or by mobile maintenance teams. Therefore locomotives in particular may not return to their "home" depots as often as in the past.

INTRODUCTION

SCOPE

This section contains details of all locomotives which can run on Britain's national railway network, plus those of Eurotunnel. Locomotives which are owned by, for example, DB Schenker and Freightliner which have been withdrawn from service and awaiting disposal are listed in the main part of the book. Locos which are awaiting disposal at scrapyards are listed in the "Locomotives Awaiting Disposal" section.

Only preserved locomotives which are currently used on the National Rail network are included. Others, which may still be Network Rail registered but not at present certified for use, are not included, but will be found in the Platform 5 book, "Preserved Locomotives and Multiple Units".

LOCOMOTIVE CLASSES

Locomotive classes are listed in numerical order of class. Principal details and dimensions are quoted for each class in metric and/or imperial units as considered appropriate bearing in mind common UK usage.

All dimensions and weights are quoted for locomotives in an "as new" condition with all necessary supplies (eg oil, water and sand) on board. Dimensions are quoted in the order length x width. Lengths quoted are over buffers or couplers as appropriate. All widths quoted are maxima. Where two different wheel diameter dimensions are shown, the first refers to powered wheels and the second refers to non-powered wheels. All weights are shown as metric tonnes (t = tonnes).

NUMERICAL LISTINGS

Locomotives are listed in numerical order. Where numbers actually carried are different from those officially allocated, these are noted in class headings where appropriate. Where locomotives have been recently renumbered, the most immediate previous number is shown in parentheses. Each locomotive entry is laid out as in the following example:

RSL No. Detail Livery Owner Pool   Allocn.   Name

60007 +* **DB** DB WFMU   TO   The Spirit of Tom Kendell

Detail Differences. Only detail differences which currently affect the areas and types of train which locomotives may work are shown. All other detail differences are excluded. Where such differences occur within a class or part class, they are shown in the "Detail" column alongside the individual locomotive number.

Standard abbreviations used for the locomotives section are:

a	Train air brake equipment only.
b	Drophead buckeye couplers.
c	Scharfenberg couplers.
d	Fitted with retractable Dellner couplers.
e	European Railway Traffic Management System (ERTMS) signalling equipment fitted.
i	Fitted with Tightlock couplers
k	Fitted with Swinghead Automatic "buckeye" combination couplers.
p	Train air, vacuum and electro-pneumatic brakes.
r	Radio Electric Token Block signalling equipment fitted.
s	Slow Speed Control equipment.
v	Train vacuum brake only.
x	Train air and vacuum brakes ("Dual brakes").
+	Additional fuel tank capacity.
§	Sandite laying equipment.

In all cases use of the above abbreviations indicates the equipment indicated is normally operable. Meaning of non-standard abbreviations and symbols is detailed in individual class headings.

Codes: Codes are used to denote the livery, owner, pool and depot of each locomotive. Details of these will be found in section 7 of this book. (S) denotes that the locomotive is currently stored.

Names: Only names carried with official sanction are listed. Names are shown in UPPER/lower case characters as actually shown on the name carried on the locomotive.

GENERAL INFORMATION

CLASSIFICATION AND NUMBERING

All locomotives are classified and allocated numbers by the Rolling Stock Library under the TOPS numbering system, introduced in 1972. This comprises a two-digit class number followed by a three-digit serial number. Where the actual number carried by a locomotive differs from the allocated number, or where an additional number is carried to the allocated number, this is shown by a note in the class heading.

For diesel locomotives, class numbers offer an indication of engine horsepower as shown in the table below.

Class No. Range	Engine hp
01–14	0–799
15–20	800–1000
21–31	1001–1499
32–39	1500–1999
40–54, 57	2000–2999
55–56, 58–70	3000+

For electric locomotives class numbers are allocated in ascending numerical order under the following scheme:

Class 71–80   Direct current and DC/diesel dual system locomotives.
Class 81 onwards   Alternating current and AC/DC dual system locos.

Numbers in the 89xxx series are allocated by the Rolling Stock Library to locomotives which have been deregistered but subsequently re-registered for use on the Network Rail network and whose original number has already been reused. 89xxx numbers are normally only carried inside locomotive cabs and are not carried externally in normal circumstances.

WHEEL ARRANGEMENT

For main line locomotives the number of driven axles on a bogie or frame is denoted by a letter (A = 1, B = 2, C = 3 etc) and the number of non-powered axles is denoted by a number. The use of the letter "o" after a letter indicates each axle is individually powered, whilst the "+" symbol indicates bogies are inter-coupled.

For shunting locomotives, the Whyte notation is used. In this notation the number of leading wheels are given, followed by the number of driving wheels and then the trailing wheels.

HAULAGE CAPABILITY OF DIESEL LOCOMOTIVES

The haulage capability of a diesel locomotive depends upon three basic factors:

1. Adhesive weight. The greater the weight on the driving wheels, the greater the adhesion and more tractive power can be applied before wheelslip occurs.

2. The characteristics of its transmission. To start a train the locomotive has to exert a pull at standstill. A direct drive diesel engine cannot do this, hence the need for transmission. This may be mechanical, hydraulic or electric. The present British Standard for locomotives is electric transmission. Here the diesel engine drives a generator or alternator and the current produced is fed to the traction motors. The force produced by each driven wheel depends on the current in its traction motor. In other words, the larger the current, the harder it pulls. As the locomotive speed increases, the current in the traction motor falls, hence the *Maximum Tractive Effort* is the maximum force at its wheels the locomotive can exert at a standstill. The electrical equipment cannot take such high currents for long without overheating. Hence the *Continuous Tractive Effort* is quoted which represents the current which the equipment can take continuously.

3. The power of its engine. Not all power reaches the rail, as electrical machines are approximately 90% efficient. As the electrical energy passes through two such machines (the generator or alternator and the traction motors), the *Power at Rail* is approximately 81% (90% of 90%) of the engine power, less a further amount used for auxiliary equipment such as radiator fans, traction motor blowers, air compressors, battery charging, cab heating, Electric Train Supply (ETS) etc. The power of the locomotive is proportional to the tractive effort times the speed. Hence when on full power there is a speed corresponding to the continuous tractive effort.

HAULAGE CAPABILITY OF ELECTRIC LOCOMOTIVES

Unlike a diesel locomotive, an electric locomotive does not develop its power on board and its performance is determined only by two factors, namely its weight and the characteristics of its electrical equipment. Whereas a diesel locomotive tends to be a constant power machine, the power of an electric locomotive varies considerably. Up to a certain speed it can produce virtually a constant tractive effort. Hence power rises with speed according to the formula given in section three above, until a maximum speed is reached at which tractive effort falls, such that the power also falls. Hence the power at the speed corresponding to the maximum tractive effort is lower than the maximum speed.

BRAKE FORCE

The brake force is a measure of the braking power of a locomotive. This is shown on the locomotive data panels so operating staff can ensure sufficient brake power is available on freight trains.

ELECTRIC TRAIN SUPPLY (ETS)

A number of locomotives are equipped to provide a supply of electricity to the train being hauled to power auxiliaries such as heating, cooling fans, air conditioning and kitchen equipment. ETS is provided from the locomotive by means of a separate alternator (except Class 33 locomotives, which have a DC generator). The ETS index of a locomotive is a measure of the electrical power available for train supply.

Similarly, most loco-hauled coaches also have an ETS index, which in this case is a measure of the power required to operate equipment mounted in the coach. The sum of the ETS indices of all the hauled vehicles in a train must not exceed the ETS index of the locomotive.

ETS is commonly (but incorrectly) known as ETH (Electric Train Heating), which is a throwback to the days before loco-hauled coaches were equipped with electrically powered auxiliary equipment other than for train heating.

ROUTE AVAILABILITY (RA)

This is a measure of a railway vehicle's axle load. The higher the axle load of a vehicle, the higher the RA number on a scale from 1 to 10. Each Network Rail route has a RA number and in general no vehicle with a higher RA number may travel on that route without special clearance.

MULTIPLE & PUSH-PULL WORKING

Multiple working between vehicles (ie two or more powered vehicles being driven from one cab) is facilitated by jumper cables connecting the vehicles. However, not all types are compatible with each other, and a number of different systems are in use, each system being incompatible with any other.

Association of American Railroads (AAR) System: Classes 59, 66, 67 and 70.
Blue Star Coupling Code: Classes 20, 25, 31, 33, 37 40 and 73.
DRS System: Classes 20/3, 37, 47 and 57.
Green Circle Coupling Code: Class 47 (not all equipped).
Orange Square Coupling Code: Class 50.
Red Diamond Coupling Code: Classes 56 and 58.
SR System: Classes 33/1, 73 and various electric multiple units.
Within Own Class only: Classes 43 and 60.

Many locomotives use a time-division multiplex (TDM) system for push-pull and multiple working which utilises the existing RCH jumper cables fitted to coaching stock vehicles. Previously these cables had only been used to control train lighting and public address systems.

Class 47 locos 47701–47717 were equipped with an older non-standard TDM system.

1. DIESEL LOCOMOTIVES

CLASS 08   BR/ENGLISH ELECTRIC   0-6-0

Built: 1955–62 by BR at Crewe, Darlington, Derby Locomotive, Doncaster or Horwich Works.
Engine: English Electric 6KT of 298 kW (400 hp) at 680 rpm.
Main Generator: English Electric 801.
Traction Motors: Two English Electric 506.
Maximum Tractive Effort: 156 kN (35000 lbf).
Continuous Tractive Effort: 49 kN (11100 lbf) at 8.8 mph.
Power At Rail: 194 kW (260 hp).   **Train Brakes:** Air & vacuum.
Brake Force: 19 t.   **Dimensions:** 8.92 x 2.59 m.
Weight: 49.6–50.4 t.   **Wheel Diameter:** 1372 mm.
Design Speed: 20 mph.   **Maximum Speed:** 15 mph.
Fuel Capacity: 3037 litres.   **RA:** 5.
Train Supply: Not equipped.
Multiple Working: m Equipped for multiple working. All others not equipped.

† – Fitted with remote control equipment.

For shunting locomotives, instead of the two-letter depot code, actual locations at the time of publication are given.

Class 08s that don't have current Network Rail engineering acceptance are considered to be "in industrial service" and can be found in section 4 of this book.

08850 has acceptance for use between Battersby and Whitby only, for rescue purposes.

Non-standard liveries/numbering:

08480   Yellow with a red bodyside band. Carries number "TOTON No 1".
08616   Carries number 3783.
08696   Carries no number.
08701   Carries number "Tyne 100".
08721   As **B**, but with a black roof & "Express parcels" branding with red & yellow stripe.
08824   Carries number "IEMD01".

Originally numbered in series D3000–D4192.

Class 08/0. Standard Design.

08077	**FL**	P	DHLT	LH Group, Barton-under-Needwood (S)
08405 a†	**E**	DB	WSSL	Dagenham Yard
08410 a	**FB**	FW	EFSH	Penzance Long Rock Depot
08428 ak	**E**	DB	WSSI	Immingham Depot
08451	**B**	AM	ATLO	Manchester Longsight Depot
08454	**K**	AM	ATLO	Manchester Longsight Depot
08472 a	**WA**	WA	RFSH	Edinburgh Craigentinny Depot
08480 a	**0**	DB	WSXX	Toton Depot

▲ EWS-liveried 08633 (which is remote-control fitted) waits its next turn at Westbury on 04/07/12.   **Tony Christie**

▼ One of two 08s based at Inverness, 08788, turns one of the ScotRail Caledonian Sleeper coaches in the station on 31/07/13.   **Alexander Colley**

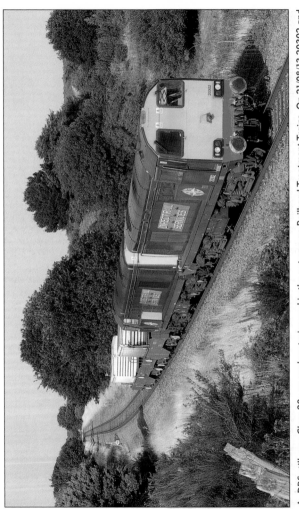

▲ DRS still uses Class 20s on nuclear trains and in the autumn on Railhead Treatment Trains. On 21/08/13 20302 and 20312 trundle along the East Suffolk Line at Eyke, between Saxmundham and Melton, with 6M69 15.42 Sizewell–Willesden nuclear flasks.

Aubrey Evans

▲ BR Blue-liveried 20107 and 20096 top-and-tail two tanks used as barrier vehicles with 20905/901 at East Goscote, between Syston and Melton Mowbray, on 26/07/13. The train was a 7Z23 17.21 Old Dalby–Barrow Hill.　**Paul Biggs**

▼ Network Rail still uses Class 31s on test trains. On 26/08/13 31233 works a 3Z01 Derby–Westbury at Charfield, Gloucestershire.　**Jamie Squibbs**

▲ West Coast Railway Company-liveried 33207 "Jim Martin" pilots GWR 5029 "Nunney Castle" on the 08.20 Bristol Temple Meads–Weymouth "Seaside Express" railtour at Hawkeridge Junction near Westbury on 28/07/13. **Mark Few**

▼ DRS-liveried 37402 and 37608 work a lightweight 6K73 08.50 Sellafield–Crewe nuclear flask train at Kirkhead Wood near Kents Bank on 06/04/13. **Tom McAtee**

▲ Network Rail-yellow-liveried 97304 "John Tiley" slowly heads along the Roxby Gullet branch from Scunthorpe with the Radio Survey Train from Derby on 29/09/13. 97303 was on the rear. **Andrew Mason**

▲ CrossCountry-liveried 43321 heads away from Plymouth with the 12.23 Plymouth–Glasgow Central on 05/04/13. **Robert Pritchard**

▼ Grand Central-liveried 43467 brings up the rear of the 17.31 Sunderland–London King's Cross at York on 06/08/12. **Robert Pritchard**

▲ Colas Rail-liveried 47749 "Demelza" approaches Teignmouth with 6Z29 12.42 Newton Abbot–Westbury engineers train on 10/09/13. **David Hunt**

▼ D1015 "Western Champion" returned to the main line in summer 2013. On 07/09/13 it approaches Weymouth with the 05.53 Leicester–Weymouth "Western Wessexman" railtour. **David Hunt**

▲ Carrying the new Devon & Cornwall Railways metallic grey livery, 56312 passes Dudley, near Cramlington, with 6Z17 15.00 Butterwell–York Holgate Sidings loaded coal on 01/10/13.

Jimmy **Wilson**

08483 a	GL	FW	EFSH	Old Oak Common HST Depot
08495 †	E	DB	WSSK	Eastleigh Yards
08500	E	DB	WNYX	Tees Yard (S)
08523	RS	RL	MRSO	Inverness Depot
08525	ST	EM	EMSL	Leeds Neville Hill Depot
08530	FL	P	DFLS	Southampton Maritime FLT
08531 a	FL	P	DFLS	Tilbury FLT
08567 †	E	DB	WNYX	Crewe International Depot (S)
08571 a	WA	WA	HBSH	Bounds Green Depot
08575	FL	P	DHLT	Southampton Maritime FLT (S)
08578 †	E	DB	WNXX	Toton Depot (S)
08580	E	DB	WSSK	Bescot Depot (S)
08585	FL	P	DFLS	Felixstowe FLT
08593	E	DB	WNXX	Crewe International Depot (S)
08596 a†	WA	WA	HBSH	Bounds Green Depot
08605 †	E	DB	WSSK	Carlisle Yards
08611	V	AM	ATLO	Manchester Longsight Depot
08615	WA	WA	RFSH	Edinburgh Craigentinny Depot
08616	LM	LM	EJLO	Birmingham Tyseley Depot
08617	K	AM	ATLO	Wembley Depot
08623	E	DB	WSSK	Bescot Yards
08624	FL	P	DFLS	Trafford Park FLT
08630	E	DB	WNXX	Toton Yards (S)
08632 †	E	DB	WSSK	Toton Yards
08633 †	E	DB	WSSK	Westbury Yards
08641	FB	FW	EFSH	Plymouth Laira Depot
08644	FB	FW	EFSH	Plymouth Laira Depot
08645	FB	FW	EFSH	Plymouth Laira Depot
08653	E	DB	WNXX	Toton Yards (S)
08663 a	FB	FW	EFSH	Bristol St Philip's Marsh Depot
08669 a	WA	WA	RFSH	Wabtec Rail, Doncaster Works
08676	E	DB	WSSL	Mossend Yard
08690	ST	EM	EMSL	Leeds Neville Hill Depot
08691	FL	FL	DFLS	Tilbury FLT
08696 a	G	AM	ATLO	Glasgow Polmadie Depot
08701 a†	RX	DB	WNXX	Toton Yards (S)
08703 a	E	DB	WSSK	Doncaster Yards
08706 †	E	DB	WNYX	Crewe International Depot (S)
08709	E	DB	WNXX	Bescot Depot (S)
08711 k	RX	DB	WNXX	Tees Yard (S)
08714	E	DB	WSXX	Axiom Rail, Stoke-on-Trent Works
08721	O	AM	ATLO	Liverpool Edge Hill Depot
08724	WA	WA	HBSH	Wabtec Rail, Doncaster Works
08735 †	E	DB	WNYX	Eastleigh Yards (S)
08737 a†	E	DB	WNYX	Crewe International Depot (S)
08738 m	ECR	DB	WNTS	Toton Yards (S)
08742 †	RX	DB	WSSK	Hoo Junction Yards
08752 †	E	DB	WSSK	Didcot Yards
08754	B	RL	MRSO	Norwich Crown Point Depot
08757 †	RG	DB	WNYX	Crewe International Depot (S)
08782 a†	CU	DB	WSSK	Doncaster Yards

08784 †	**E**	DB	WNTS	Toton Depot (S)
08785 a	**FL**	P	DFLS	Southampton Maritime FLT
08788	**K**	AM	MRSO	Inverness Depot
08790	**B**	AM	ATLO	Wolverhampton Oxley Depot
08795	**GL**	FW	EFSH	Swansea Landore Depot
08799 a	**E**	DB	WSSK	Hoo Junction Yards
08802 †	**E**	DB	WNYX	Doncaster Yards (S)
08804 †	**E**	DB	WNYX	Crewe International Depot (S)
08805	**B**	LM	EJLO	Birmingham Soho Depot
08822	**FB**	FW	EFSH	Bristol St Philip's Marsh Depot
08824 ak	**K**	DB	WSXX	Crewe International Depot
08836	**FB**	FW	EFSH	Old Oak Common HST Depot
08847	**CD**	RL	MRSO	Allely's Heavy Haulage, Studley, Warks
08850	**B**	NY	MBDL	Grosmont Depot
08853 a	**WA**	WA	RFSH	Wabtec Rail, Doncaster Works
08865	**E**	DB	WNYX	Crewe International Depot (S)
08874	**SL**	RL	MRSO	Norwich Crown Point Depot
08877	**DG**	DB	WSXX	Wigan Springs Branch Depot
08879 †	**E**	DB	WSSK	Hinksey Yard
08886	**E**	DB	WNXX	Crewe International Depot (S)
08887 a	**B**	AM	ATLO	Wembley Depot
08888 †	**E**	DB	WSSI	Margam Yard
08891	**FL**	P	DHLT	LH Group, Barton-under-Needwood (S)
08899	**MA**	EM	EMSL	Derby Etches Park Depot
08904	**E**	DB	WNYX	Crewe International Depot (S)
08907	**E**	DB	WSSK	Bescot Yards
08908	**ST**	EM	EMSL	Leeds Neville Hill Depot
08922	**DG**	DB	WNTS	Toton Depot (S)
08925	**G**	GB	GBWM	March Whitemoor Yard
08934 a	**VP**	GB	GBWM	Cardiff Tidal Steelworks
08939 m	**ECR**	DB	WNTS	Toton Yards (S)
08948 c	**EP**	EU	GPSS	Temple Mills Depot
08950	**ST**	EM	EMSL	Leeds Neville Hill Depot

Class 08/9. Reduced height cab. Converted 1985–87 by BR at Landore.

08993	**E**	DB	WNTS	Doncaster Depot (S)
08994 a	**E**	DB	WNTS	Toton Depot (S)
08995 a	**E**	DB	WNYX	Crewe International Depot (S)

CLASS 09   BR/ENGLISH ELECTRIC   0-6-0

Built: 1959–62 by BR at Darlington or Horwich Works.
Engine: English Electric 6KT of 298 kW (400 hp) at 680 rpm.
Main Generator: English Electric 801.
Traction Motors: English Electric 506.
Maximum Tractive Effort: 111 kN (25000 lbf).
Continuous Tractive Effort: 39 kN (8800 lbf) at 11.6 mph.

Power At Rail: 201 kW (269 hp).	**Train Brakes:** Air & vacuum.
Brake Force: 19 t.	**Dimensions:** 8.92 x 2.59 m.
Weight: 49 t.	**Wheel Diameter:** 1372 mm.
Design Speed: 27 mph.	**Maximum Speed:** 27 mph.
Fuel Capacity: 3037 litres.	**RA:** 5.
Train Supply: Not equipped.	**Multiple Working:** Not equipped.

Class 09s that don't have current Network Rail engineering acceptance are
considered to be "in industrial service" and can be found in section 4 of this
book.

Class 09/0 were originally numbered D3665–D3671, D3719–D3721, D4099–
D4114.

Class 09/0. Built as Class 09.

09002	**G**	GB	GBWM	March Whitemoor Yard
09006	**E**	DB	WNXX	Doncaster Depot (S)
09009	**G**	GB	GBWM	Trafford Park FLT
09026 a	**G**	SN	HWSU	Brighton Lovers Walk Depot

Class 09/1. Converted from Class 08. 110 V electrical equipment.
Converted: 1992–1993 by RFS Industries, Kilnhurst.

09106 (08759)		**E**	DB	WSSK	Warrington Yards

Class 09/2. Converted from Class 08. 90 V electrical equipment.
Converted: 1992 by RFS Industries, Kilnhurst.

09201 (08421) ak†	**DG**	DB	WSSI	Knottingley Depot

Class 08 and Class 09 names:

08451	M.A. SMITH	08691	Terri
08483	DUSTY Driver David Miller	08721	DOWNHILL C.S.
08495	NOEL KIRTON OBE	08782	CASTLETON WORKS
08525	DUNCAN BEDFORD	08790	Steve Purser
08585	Vicky	08799	FRED
08616	TYSELEY 100	08805	CONCORDE
08630	BOB BROWN	08822	John
08645	Mike Baggott	08874	Catherine
08663	Jack	08908	IVAN STEPHENSON
08669	Bob Machin	08950	DAVID LIGHTFOOT
08690	DAVID THIRKILL	09026	Cedric Wares

CLASS 20   ENGLISH ELECTRIC   Bo-Bo

Built: 1957–68 by English Electric at Vulcan Foundry, Newton-le-Willows or by Robert Stephenson & Hawthorns at Darlington.
Engine: English Electric 8SVT Mk II of 746 kW (1000 hp) at 850 rpm.
Main Generator: English Electric 819/3C.
Traction Motors: English Electric 526/5D or 526/8D.
Maximum Tractive Effort: 187 kN (42000 lbf).
Continuous Tractive Effort: 111 kN (25000 lbf) at 11 mph.
Power At Rail: 574 kW (770 hp).   **Train Brakes:** Air & vacuum.
Brake Force: 35 t.   **Dimensions:** 14.25 x 2.67 m.
Weight: 73.4–73.5 t.   **Wheel Diameter:** 1092 mm.
Design Speed: 75 mph.   **Maximum Speed:** 75 mph.
Fuel Capacity: 1727 litres.   **RA:** 5.
Train Supply: Not equipped.   **Multiple Working:** Blue Star.

Originally numbered in series D8007–D8190, D8315–D8325.

Non-standard liveries/numbering:

20088 RFS grey (carries No. 2017).
20189 London Underground red. Also carries No. L189.
20227 White, red & blue with London Underground roundels.

Class 20/0. Standard Design.

20016	B	HN	HNRS	LM (S)	
20057	B	HN	HNRS	BH (S)	
20081	B	HN	HNRS	LM (S)	
20088	0	HN	HNRS	LM (S)	
20092	U	HN	HNRS	LM (S)	
20096	B	HN	GBEE	BH	
20107	B	HN	GBEE	BH	
20118	F0	HN	HNRL	BH	Saltburn-by-the-Sea
20132	F0	HN	HNRL	BH	
20142	B	20	GBEE	SK	
20189	0	20	GBEE	SK	
20227	0	2L	GBEE	SK	

Class 20/3. Direct Rail Services refurbished locos. Details as Class 20/0 except:

Refurbished: 15 locomotives were refurbished 1995–96 by Brush Traction at Loughborough (20301–305) or 1997–98 by RFS(E) at Doncaster (20306–315). Disc indicators or headcode panels removed.
Train Brakes: Air.   **Maximum Speed:** 60 mph (+ 75 mph).
Weight: 73 t (+ 76 t).   **Fuel Capacity:** 2909 (+ 4909) litres.
Brake Force: 35 t (+ 31 t).   **RA:** 5 (+ 6).
Multiple Working: DRS system.

20301	(20047) r	**DS**	DR	XHNC	KM	Max Joule 1958–1999
20302	(20084) r	**DS**	DR	XHNC	KM	
20303	(20127) r	**DS**	DR	XHNC	KM	
20304	(20120) r	**DS**	DR	XHNC	KM	
20305	(20095) r	**DS**	DR	XHNC	KM	Gresty Bridge
20308	(20187) r+	**DS**	DR	XHNC	KM	

```
20309 (20075) r+   DS  DR  XHNC        KM
20311 (20102) r+   HN  HN  GBEE        BH
20312 (20042) r+   DS  DR  XHNC        KM
20314 (20117) r+   HN  HN  GBEE        BH
```

Class 20/9. Harry Needle Railroad Company (former Hunslet-Barclay/DRS) locos. Details as Class 20/0 except:

Refurbished: 1989 by Hunslet-Barclay at Kilmarnock.
Train Brakes: Air.   **Fuel Capacity:** 1727 (+ 4727) litres.
RA: 5 (+ 6).

```
20901 (20101)      GB  HN  GBEE        BH
20903 (20083) +    DR  HN  HNRS        BO (S)
20904 (20041) +    DR  HN  HNRS        BO (S)
20905 (20225) +    GB  HN  GBEE        BH
```

CLASS 25   BR/BEYER PEACOCK/SULZER   Bo-Bo

Built: 1965 by Beyer Peacock at Gorton.
Engine: Sulzer 6LDA28-B of 930 kW (1250 hp) at 750 rpm.
Main Generator: AEI RTB15656.   **Traction Motors:** AEI 253AY.
Maximum Tractive Effort: 200 kN (45000 lbf).
Continuous Tractive Effort: 93 kN (20800 lbf) at 17.1 mph.
Power At Rail: 708 kW (949 hp).   **Train Brakes:** Air & vacuum.
Brake Force: 38 t.   **Dimensions:** 15.39 × 2.73 m.
Weight: 71.5 t.   **Wheel Diameter:** 1143 mm.
Design Speed: 90 mph.   **Maximum Speed:** 60 mph.
Fuel Capacity: 2270 litres.   **RA:** 5.
Train Supply: Not equipped.   **Multiple Working:** Blue Star.

Original number is D7628, which the loco currently carries.

Only certified for use on Network Rail metals between Whitby and Battersby, as an extension of North Yorkshire Moors Railway services.

```
25278        GG  NY  MBDL        NY      SYBILLA
```

CLASS 31   BRUSH/ENGLISH ELECTRIC   A1A-A1A

Built: 1958–62 by Brush Traction at Loughborough.
Engine: English Electric 12SVT of 1100 kW (1470 hp) at 850 rpm.
Main Generator: Brush TG160-48.   **Traction Motors:** Brush TM73-68.
Maximum Tractive Effort: 160 kN (35900 lbf).
Continuous Tractive Effort: 83 kN (18700 lbf) at 23.5 mph.
Power At Rail: 872 kW (1170 hp).   **Train Brakes:** Air & vacuum.
Brake Force: 49 t.   **Dimensions:** 17.30 × 2.67 m.
Weight: 106.7–111 t.   **Wheel Diameter:** 1092/1003 mm.
Design Speed: 90 mph.   **Maximum Speed:** 90 mph.
Fuel Capacity: 2409 litres.   **RA:** 5 or 6.
Train Supply: Not equipped.   **Multiple Working:** Blue Star.

Originally numbered D5520–D5699, D5800–D5862 (not in order).

Non-standard numbering: 31190 Also carries number D5613.

Class 31/1. Standard Design. RA: 5.

31105	**Y**	NR	QADD	ZA	
31106 a	**B**	HJ	RVLO	ZA	
31128	**B**	NS	NRLO	NY	CHARYBDIS
31190	**G**	BA	HTLX	WH	
31233 a	**Y**	NR	QADD	ZA	
31285	**Y**	NR	QADD	ZA	

Class 31/4. Electric Train Supply equipment. RA: 6.
Train Supply: Electric, index 66.

31422	**IC**	RE	RVLO	ZA (S)	
31452	**DC**	BA	HTLX	ZA	
31454	**IC**	BA	HTLX	WH	
31459	**K**	RE	RVLO	ZA	CERBERUS
31465	**Y**	NR	QADD	ZA	
31468	**FR**	BA	RVLO	WO (S)	HYDRA

Class 31/6. ETS through wiring and controls. RA: 5.

31601 (31186)	**DC**	BA	HTLX	WH	
31602 (31191)	**Y**	BA	HTLX	WO (S)	

CLASS 33   BRCW/SULZER   Bo-Bo

Built: 1960–62 by the Birmingham Railway Carriage & Wagon Company at Smethwick.
Engine: Sulzer 8LDA28 of 1160 kW (1550 hp) at 750 rpm.
Main Generator: Crompton Parkinson CG391B1.
Traction Motors: Crompton Parkinson C171C2.
Maximum Tractive Effort: 200 kN (45000 lbf).
Continuous Tractive Effort: 116 kN (26000 lbf) at 17.5 mph.

Power At Rail: 906 kW (1215 hp).	**Train Brakes:** Air & vacuum.
Brake Force: 35 t.	**Dimensions:** 15.47 x 2.82 (2.64 m 33/2).
Weight: 76-78 t.	**Wheel Diameter:** 1092 mm.
Design Speed: 85 mph.	**Maximum Speed:** 85 mph.
Fuel Capacity: 3410 litres.	**RA:** 6.

Train Supply: Electric, index 48 (750 V DC only).
Multiple Working: Blue Star.

Originally numbered in series D6500–D6597 but not in order.

Non-standard numbering: 33012 Carries number D6515.

Class 33/0. Standard Design.

33012	**G**	71	MBDL	Swanage Rly	
33025	**WC**	WC	AWCX	SH (S)	Glen Falloch
33029	**WC**	WC	AWCA	CS	Glen Loy
33030	**DR**	WC	AWCX	CS (S)	

Class 33/2. Built to former Loading Gauge of Tonbridge–Battle Line.
Equipped with slow speed control.

33207	**WC**	WC	AWCA	CS	Jim Martin

CLASS 37   ENGLISH ELECTRIC   Co-Co

Built: 1960–66 by English Electric at Vulcan Foundry, Newton-le-Willows or by Robert Stephenson & Hawthorns at Darlington.
Engine: English Electric 12CSVT of 1300 kW (1750 hp) at 850 rpm.
Main Generator: English Electric 822/10G.
Traction Motors: English Electric 538/A.
Maximum Tractive Effort: 245 kN (55500 lbf).
Continuous Tractive Effort: 156 kN (35000 lbf) at 13.6 mph.
Power At Rail: 932 kW (1250 hp).   **Train Brakes:** Air & vacuum.
Brake Force: 50 t.   **Dimensions:** 18.75 x 2.74 m.
Weight: 102.8–108.4 t.   **Wheel Diameter:** 1092 mm.
Design Speed: 90 mph.   **Maximum Speed:** 80 mph.
Fuel Capacity: 4046 (+ 7683) litres. **RA:** 5 (§ 6).
Train Supply: Not equipped.
Multiple Working: Blue Star († DRS system).

Originally numbered D6600–D6608, D6700–D6999 (not in order).

Class 37/0. Standard Design. Details as above.

37038	a†	**DR**	DR	XHNC	KM
37059	ar+†**DS**		DR	XHSS	Daventry
37069	ar+†**DS**		DR	XHSS	Daventry
37165	a+	**CE**	WC	AWCX	CS (S)
37194	a+†**DS**		DR	XHNC	KM
37198	+	**Y**	NR	MBDL	GCR (S)
37214		**WC**	WC	AWCX	CS (S)
37218	ar+†**DS**		DR	XHNC	KM
37259	ar†	**DS**	DR	XHNC	KM
37261	a+	**DS**	DR	XHNC	KM

Class 37/4. Refurbished with electric train supply equipment. Main generator replaced by alternator. Regeared (CP7) bogies. Details as Class 37/0 except:
Main Alternator: Brush BA1005A.   **Power At Rail:** 935 kW (1254 hp).
Traction Motors: English Electric 538/5A.
Maximum Tractive Effort: 256 kN (57440 lbf).
Continuous Tractive Effort: 184 kN (41250 lbf) at 11.4 mph.
Weight: 107 t.   **Design Speed:** 80 mph.
Fuel Capacity: 7683 litres.
Train Supply: Electric, index 30.

37401	ar	**E**	DR	XHHP	Bo'ness	
37402	a	**DS**	DR	XHAC	KM	
37405	ar	**DS**	DR	XHAC	KM	
37409	ar†	**DS**	DR	XHAC	KM	Lord Hinton
37419	ar	**DS**	DR	XHAC	KM	Carl Haviland 1954–2012
37422	ar	**E**	DR	XHHP	ZH (S)	
37423	ar†	**DS**	DR	XHAC	KM	Spirit of the Lakes
37425	ar	**DS**	DR	XHAC	KM	Sir Robert McAlpine/Concrete Bob

Class 37/5. Refurbished without train supply equipment. Main generator replaced by alternator. Regeared (CP7) bogies. Details as Class 37/4 except:
Maximum Tractive Effort: 248 kN (55590 lbf).
Weight: 106.1–110.0 t.

37503	r§	**E**	DR	XHSS	BH (S)
37510	a	**DS**	DR	XHSS	BH (S)
37516	s	**WC**	WC	AWCA	CS	Loch Laidon
37517	as	**LH**	WC	AWCX	CS (S)
37518	ar	**IC**	IR	MBDL	BQ	Fort William/An Gearasdan
37521	r§	**E**	DR	XHSS	BH (S)	English China Clays

Class 37/6. Originally refurbished for Nightstar services. Main generator replaced by alternator. UIC jumpers. Details as Class 37/5 except:
Maximum Speed: 90 mph.   **Train Brake:** Air.
Train Supply: Not equipped, but electric through wired.
Multiple Working: DRS system.

37601	a	**DS**	DR	XHNC	KM	Class 37-'Fifty'
37602	ar	**DS**	DR	XHNC	KM
37603	a	**DS**	DR	XHNC	KM
37604	a	**DS**	DR	XHNC	KM
37605	ar	**DS**	DR	XHNC	KM
37606	a	**DS**	DR	XHNC	KM
37607	ar	**DS**	DR	XHNC	KM
37608	ar	**DS**	DR	XHNC	KM
37609	a	**DS**	DR	XHNC	KM
37610	a	**DS**	DR	XHNC	KM
37611	a	**DS**	DR	XHNC	KM
37612	a	**DS**	DR	XHNC	KM

Class 37/5 continued.

37667	ars†	**DS**	DR	XHNC	KM
37668	s	**E**	WC	AWCX	CS (S)
37669	r	**E**	WC	AWCX	CS (S)
37670	r	**DB**	DR	XHSS	KG (S)
37676	a	**WC**	WC	AWCA	CS	Loch Rannoch
37682	ar	**DS**	DR	XHNC	KM
37685	a	**WC**	WC	AWCA	CS	Loch Arkaig
37688	ar†	**DS**	DR	XHNC	KM	Kingmoor TMD
37696	as	**F**	DR	XHSS	CF Booth's, Rotherham

Class 37/7. Refurbished locos. Main generator replaced by alternator. Regeared (CP7) bogies. Ballast weights added. Details as Class 37/5 except:
Main Alternator: GEC G564AZ (37796–803) Brush BA1005A (others).
Maximum Tractive Effort: 276 kN (62000 lbf).
Weight: 120 t.   **RA:** 7.

37703		**GIF**	DR	XHHP	BH (S)
37706		**WC**	WC	AWCA	CS
37710		**LH**	WC	AWCX	CS (S)
37712	a	**WC**	WC	AWCX	CS (S)
37714		**GIF**	DR	XHHP	BH (S)

37716	**GIF**	DR	XHHP	ZA (S)
37718	**GIF**	DR	XHHP	ZA (S)
37800	**GIF**	EP	EPUK	WH (S)
37884	**GIF**	EP	EPUK	WH (S)

Class 97/3. Class 37s refurbished for Network Rail for use on the Cambrian Lines which are signalled by ERTMS. Details as Class 37/0.

97301	(37100)	e	**Y**	NR	QETS	ZA	
97302	(37170)	e	**Y**	NR	QETS	ZA	
97303	(37178)	e	**Y**	NR	QETS	ZA	
97304	(37217)	e	**Y**	NR	QETS	ZA	John Tiley

CLASS 40   ENGLISH ELECTRIC   1Co-Co1

Built: 1958–62 by English Electric at Vulcan Foundry, Newton-le-Willows.
Engine: English Electric 16SVT Mk2 of 1490 kW (2000 hp) at 850 rpm.
Main Generator: English Electric 822/4C.
Traction Motors: English Electric 526/5D or EE526/7D.
Maximum Tractive Effort: 231 kN (52000 lbf).
Continuous Tractive Effort: 137 kN (30900 lbf) at 18.8 mph.
Power At Rail: 1160 kW (1550 hp).   **Train Brakes:** Air & vacuum.
Brake Force: 51 t.   **Dimensions:** 21.18 x 2.78 m.
Weight: 132 t.   **Wheel Diameter:** 914/1143 mm.
Design Speed: 90 mph.   **Maximum Speed:** 90 mph.
Fuel Capacity: 3250 litres.   **RA:** 6.
Train Supply: Steam.   **Multiple Working:** Blue Star.

Originally numbered D345. Currently carries No. 345.

| 40145 | **B** | 40 | ELRD | BQ |

CLASS 43   BREL/PAXMAN   Bo-Bo

Built: 1975–82 by BREL at Crewe Works.
Engine: MTU 16V4000R41R of 1680kW (2250 hp) at 1500 rpm.
(* Paxman 12VP185 of 1565 kW (2100 hp) at 1500 rpm.)
Main Alternator: Brush BA1001B.
Traction Motors: Brush TMH68–46 or GEC G417AZ, frame mounted.
Maximum Tractive Effort: 80 kN (17980 lbf).
Continuous Tractive Effort: 46 kN (10340 lbf) at 64.5 mph.
Power At Rail: 1320 kW (1770 hp).   **Train Brakes:** Air.
Brake Force: 35 t.   **Dimensions:** 17.79 x 2.74 m.
Weight: 70.25 t.   **Wheel Diameter:** 1020 mm.
Design Speed: 125 mph.   **Maximum Speed:** 125 mph.
Fuel Capacity: 4500 litres.   **RA:** 5.
Train Supply: Three-phase electric.
Multiple Working: Within class, jumpers at non-driving end only.

† Buffer fitted.

43013, 43014 & 43062 are fitted with measuring apparatus & front-end cameras.

Advertising livery: 43148 and 43186 Hewlett Packard (white).

43002	**FB**	A	EFPC	LA	
43003	**FB**	A	EFPC	LA	ISAMBARD KINGDOM BRUNEL
43004	**FB**	A	EFPC	LA	First for the future/
					First ar gyfer y dyfodol
43005	**FB**	A	EFPC	LA	
43009	**FB**	A	EFPC	LA	First transforming travel
43010	**FB**	A	EFPC	LA	
43012	**FB**	A	EFPC	LA	
43013 †	**Y**	P	QCAR	EC	
43014 †	**Y**	P	QCAR	EC	
43015	**FB**	A	EFPC	LA	
43016	**FB**	A	EFPC	LA	
43017	**FB**	A	EFPC	LA	
43018	**FB**	A	EFPC	LA	
43020	**FB**	A	EFPC	LA	MTU Power. Passion. Partnership
43021	**FB**	A	EFPC	LA	David Austin – Cartoonist
43022	**FB**	A	EFPC	LA	
43023	**FB**	A	EFPC	LA	
43024	**FB**	A	EFPC	LA	Great Western Society 1961–2011
					Didcot Railway Centre
43025	**FB**	A	EFPC	LA	IRO The Institution of Railway Operators
					2000–2010 TEN YEARS
					PROMOTING OPERATIONAL EXCELLENCE
43026	**FB**	A	EFPC	LA	
43027	**FB**	A	EFPC	LA	Glorious Devon
43028	**FB**	A	EFPC	LA	
43029	**FB**	A	EFPC	LA	
43030	**FB**	A	EFPC	LA	Christian Lewis Trust
43031	**FB**	A	EFPC	LA	
43032	**FB**	A	EFPC	LA	
43033	**FB**	A	EFPC	LA	Driver Brian Cooper
					15 June 1947–5 October 1999
43034	**FB**	A	EFPC	LA	TravelWatch SouthWest
43035	**FB**	A	EFPC	LA	
43036	**FB**	A	EFPC	LA	
43037	**FB**	A	EFPC	LA	PENYDARREN
43040	**FB**	A	EFPC	LA	Bristol St. Philip's Marsh
43041	**FB**	A	EFPC	OO	Meningitis Trust Support for Life
43042	**FB**	A	EFPC	OO	
43043 *	**ST**	P	EMPC	NL	
43044 *	**ST**	P	EMPC	NL	
43045 *	**ST**	P	EMPC	NL	
43046 *	**ST**	P	EMPC	NL	
43047 *	**ST**	P	EMPC	NL	
43048 *	**ST**	P	EMPC	NL	T.C.B. Miller MBE
43049 *	**ST**	P	EMPC	NL	Neville Hill

43050 *	ST	P	EMPC	NL	
43052 *	ST	P	EMPC	NL	
43053	FB	P	EFPC	LE	University of Worcester
43054 *	ST	P	EMPC	NL	
43055 *	ST	P	EMPC	NL	The Sheffield Star 125 Years
43056	FB	P	EFPC	LE	The Royal British Legion
43058 *	ST	P	EMPC	NL	
43059 *	ST	P	EMPC	NL	
43060 *	ST	P	EMPC	NL	
43061 *	ST	P	EMPC	NL	
43062	Y	P	QCAR	EC	John Armitt
43063	FB	P	EFPC	OO	
43064 *	ST	P	EMPC	NL	
43066 *	ST	P	EMPC	NL	
43069	FB	P	EFPC	OO	
43070	FB	P	EFPC	OO	The Corps of Royal Electrical and Mechanical Engineers
43071	FB	P	EFPC	OO	
43073 *	ST	P	EMPC	NL	
43075 *	ST	P	EMPC	NL	
43076 *	ST	P	EMPC	NL	IN SUPPORT OF HELP for HEROES
43078	FB	P	EFPC	OO	
43079	FB	P	EFPC	OO	
43081 *	ST	P	EMPC	NL	
43082 *	ST	P	EMPC	NL	RAILWAY children – THE VOICE FOR STREET CHILDREN WORLDWIDE
43083 *	ST	P	EMPC	NL	
43086	FB	P	EFPC	OO	
43087	FB	P	EFPC	OO	11 Explosive Ordnance Disposal Regiment Royal Logistic Corps
43088	FB	P	EFPC	OO	
43089 *	ST	P	EMPC	NL	
43091	FB	P	EFPC	OO	
43092	FB	FG	EFPC	OO	
43093	FB	FG	EFPC	OO	
43094	FB	FG	EFPC	OO	
43097	FB	FG	EFPC	OO	Environment Agency
43098	FB	FG	EFPC	OO	
43122	FB	FG	EFPC	OO	
43124	FB	A	EFPC	LE	
43125	FB	A	EFPC	LE	
43126	FB	A	EFPC	LE	
43127	FB	A	EFPC	LE	Sir Peter Parker 1924–2002 Cotswold Line 150
43128	FB	A	EFPC	LE	
43129	FB	A	EFPC	LE	
43130	FB	A	EFPC	LE	
43131	FB	A	EFPC	LE	
43132	FB	A	EFPC	LE	We Save the Children – Will You?
43133	FB	A	EFPC	LE	
43134	FB	A	EFPC	LE	

43135	**FB**	A	EFPC	LE	
43136	**FB**	A	EFPC	LE	
43137	**FB**	A	EFPC	LE	Newton Abbot 150
43138	**FB**	A	EFPC	LE	
43139	**FB**	A	EFPC	LE	Driver Stan Martin
					25 June 1950 – 6 November 2004
43140	**FB**	A	EFPC	LE	
43141	**FB**	A	EFPC	LE	
43142	**FB**	A	EFPC	LE	Reading Panel Signal Box 1965–2010
43143	**FB**	A	EFPC	LE	Stroud 700
43144	**FB**	A	EFPC	LE	
43145	**FB**	A	EFPC	LE	
43146	**FB**	A	EFPC	LE	
43147	**FB**	A	EFPC	LE	
43148	**AL**	A	EFPC	LE	
43149	**FB**	A	EFPC	LE	University of Plymouth
43150	**FB**	A	EFPC	LE	
43151	**FB**	A	EFPC	LE	
43152	**FB**	A	EFPC	LE	
43153	**FB**	FG	EFPC	OO	
43154	**FB**	FG	EFPC	OO	
43155	**FB**	FG	EFPC	OO	
43156	**FB**	P	EFPC	OO	Dartington International Summer School
43158	**FB**	FG	EFPC	OO	
43159	**FB**	P	EFPC	OO	
43160	**FB**	P	EFPC	OO	Sir Moir Lockhead OBE
43161	**FB**	P	EFPC	OO	
43162	**FB**	P	EFPC	OO	
43163	**FB**	A	EFPC	OO	Exeter Panel Signal Box
					21st Anniversary 2009
43164	**FB**	A	EFPC	OO	
43165	**FB**	A	EFPC	OO	Prince Michael of Kent
43168	**FB**	A	EFPC	OO	
43169	**FB**	A	EFPC	OO	THE NATIONAL TRUST
43170	**FB**	A	EFPC	OO	
43171	**FB**	A	EFPC	OO	
43172	**FB**	A	EFPC	OO	
43174	**FB**	A	EFPC	OO	
43175	**FB**	A	EFPC	OO	GWR 175TH ANNIVERSARY
43176	**FB**	A	EFPC	OO	
43177	**FB**	A	EFPC	OO	
43179	**FB**	A	EFPC	OO	Pride of Laira
43180	**FB**	P	EFPC	OO	
43181	**FB**	A	EFPC	OO	
43182	**FB**	A	EFPC	OO	
43183	**FB**	A	EFPC	OO	
43185	**FB**	A	EFPC	OO	Great Western
43186	**AL**	A	EFPC	OO	
43187	**FB**	A	EFPC	OO	
43188	**FB**	A	EFPC	OO	
43189	**FB**	A	EFPC	OO	RAILWAY HERITAGE TRUST

43190	**FB**	A	EFPC	OO	
43191	**FB**	A	EFPC	OO	
43192	**FB**	A	EFPC	OO	
43193	**FB**	P	EFPC	OO	
43194	**FB**	FG	EFPC	OO	
43195	**FB**	P	EFPC	OO	
43196	**FB**	P	EFPC	OO	
43197	**FB**	P	EFPC	OO	
43198	**FB**	FG	EFPC	OO	Oxfordshire 2007

Class 43/2. Rebuilt East Coast, CrossCountry and Grand Central power cars. Power cars have been renumbered by adding 200 to their original number or 400 to their original number (Grand Central) except 43123 which became 43423.

43206 (43006)	**EC**	A	IECP	EC	
43207 (43007)	**XC**	A	EHPC	EC	
43208 (43008)	**NX**	A	IECP	EC	Lincolnshire Echo
43238 (43038)	**EC**	A	IECP	EC	
43239 (43039)	**EC**	A	IECP	EC	
43251 (43051)	**EC**	P	IECP	EC	
43257 (43057)	**EC**	P	IECP	EC	
43272 (43072)	**EC**	P	IECP	EC	
43274 (43074)	**EC**	P	IECP	EC	
43277 (43077)	**EC**	P	IECP	EC	
43285 (43085)	**XC**	P	EHPC	EC	
43290 (43090)	**EC**	P	IECP	EC	mtu fascination of power
43295 (43095)	**EC**	A	IECP	EC	
43296 (43096)	**EC**	A	IECP	EC	
43299 (43099)	**EC**	P	IECP	EC	
43300 (43100)	**EC**	P	IECP	EC	Craigentinny
43301 (43101)	**XC**	P	EHPC	EC	
43302 (43102)	**EC**	P	IECP	EC	
43303 (43103)	**XC**	P	EHPC	EC	
43304 (43104)	**XC**	A	EHPC	EC	
43305 (43105)	**NX**	A	IECP	EC	
43306 (43106)	**EC**	A	IECP	EC	
43307 (43107)	**EC**	A	IECP	EC	
43308 (43108)	**EC**	A	IECP	EC	
43309 (43109)	**EC**	A	IECP	EC	
43310 (43110)	**NX**	A	IECP	EC	
43311 (43111)	**EC**	A	IECP	EC	
43312 (43112)	**NX**	A	IECP	EC	
43313 (43113)	**NX**	A	IECP	EC	
43314 (43114)	**EC**	A	IECP	EC	
43315 (43115)	**EC**	A	IECP	EC	
43316 (43116)	**EC**	A	IECP	EC	
43317 (43117)	**EC**	A	IECP	EC	
43318 (43118)	**NX**	A	IECP	EC	
43319 (43119)	**EC**	A	IECP	EC	
43320 (43120)	**NX**	A	IECP	EC	
43321 (43121)	**XC**	P	EHPC	EC	

43357	(43157)	**XC**	P	EHPC	EC	
43366	(43166)	**XC**	A	EHPC	EC	
43367	(43167)	**EC**	A	IECP	EC	DELTIC 50 1955–2005
43378	(43178)	**XC**	A	EHPC	EC	
43384	(43184)	**XC**	A	EHPC	EC	
43423	(43123) †	**GC**	A	GCHP	HT	'VALENTA' 1972–2010
43465	(43065) †	**GC**	A	GCHP	HT	
43467	(43067) †	**GC**	A	GCHP	HT	
43468	(43068) †	**GC**	A	GCHP	HT	
43480	(43080) †	**GC**	A	GCHP	HT	
43484	(43084) †	**GC**	A	GCHP	HT	PETER FOX 1942–2011 PLATFORM 5

CLASS 47   BR/BRUSH/SULZER   Co-Co

Built: 1963–67 by Brush Traction, at Loughborough or by BR at Crewe Works.
Engine: Sulzer 12LDA28C of 1920 kW (2580 hp) at 750 rpm.
Main Generator: Brush TG160-60 Mk4 or TM172-50 Mk1.
Traction Motors: Brush TM64-68 Mk1 or Mk1A.
Maximum Tractive Effort: 267 kN (60000 lbf).
Continuous Tractive Effort: 133 kN (30000 lbf) at 26 mph.
Power At Rail: 1550 kW (2080 hp).   **Train Brakes:** Air.
Brake Force: 61 t.   **Dimensions:** 19.38 x 2.79 m.
Weight: 111.5–120.6 t.   **Wheel Diameter:** 1143 mm.
Design Speed: 95 mph.
Maximum Speed: 95 mph (* 75 mph).
Fuel Capacity: 3273 (+ 5887).   **RA:** 6 or 7.
Train Supply: Not equipped.
Multiple Working: m Green Circle (operational locos only).

Originally numbered in series D1100–D1111, D1500–D1999 but not in order.

Non-standard liveries/numbering:

47270	Also carries the number 1971.
47773	Also carries the number D1755.
47812	Also carries the number D1916.
47815	Also carries the number D1748.

Class 47/0 (Dual-braked locos) or Class 47/2 (Air-braked locos). Standard Design. Details as above.

47194	a+	**F**	WC	AWCX	CS (S)	
47236	+	**FE**	WC	AWCX	CS (S)	
47237	x+	**WC**	WC	AWCA	CS	
47245	x+m	**WC**	WC	AWCA	CS	
47270	a+	**B**	PO	AWCA	CS	SWIFT

Class 47/3 (Dual-braked locos) or Class 47/2 (Air-braked locos).
Details as Class 47/0 except: **Weight:** 113.7 t.

47355	am+	**K**	WC	AWCX	CS (S)	
47368	x	**F**	WC	AWCX	CS (S)	
47375	+m	**B**	NS	NRLO	BO	TINSLEY TRACTION DEPOT

Class 47/4. Electric Train Supply equipment.
Details as Class 47/0 except:

Weight: 120.4–125.1 t.   **Fuel Capacity:** 3273 (+ 5537) litres.
Train Supply: Electric. ETH 66.   **RA:** 7.

47492	x	**RX**	WC	AWCX	CS (S)	
47500	x	**WC**	WC	AWCX	CS (S)	
47501	xm+	**DS**	DR	XHNB	KM	Craftsman
47526	x	**BL**	WC	AWCX	CS (S)	
47580	x	**BL**	47	MBDL	TM	County of Essex

Class 47/7. Former Railnet dedicated locos. All have twin fuel tanks.

47727	m	**CS**	CS	COLO	WH	Rebecca
47739	m	**CS**	CS	COLO	WH	Robin of Templecombe 1938–2013
47746	x	**WC**	WC	AWCA	CS	
47749	m	**CS**	CS	COLO	WH	Demelza
47760	x	**WC**	WC	AWCA	CS	
47768		**RX**	WC	AWCX	CS (S)	
47769		**V**	RV	RTLO	CD	Resolve
47772	x	**RX**	WC	AWCX	CS (S)	
47773	x	**GG**	70	MBDL	TM	
47776	x	**RX**	WC	AWCX	CS (S)	
47786		**WC**	WC	AWCA	CS	Roy Castle OBE
47787		**WC**	WC	AWCA	CS (S)	Windsor Castle
47790	m	**VN**	DR	XHNB	KM	Galloway Princess

Class 47/4 continued. RA6. Most fitted with extended-range fuel tanks (+).

47798	x	**RP**	NM	MBDL	YK	Prince William
47802	+m	**DS**	DR	XHAC	KM	Pride of Cumbria
47804		**WC**	WC	AWCA	CS	
47805	+m	**DS**	DR	XHAC	KM	John Scott 12.5.45–22.5.12
47810	+m	**DS**	DR	XHAC	KM	Peter Bath MBE 1927–2006
47811	+	**GL**	FL	DFLH	BA (S)	
47812	+m	**GG**	RV	RTLO	CD	
47813	+m	**DS**	DR	XHNB	KM	Solent
47815	+m	**GG**	RV	RTLO	CD	GREAT WESTERN
47816	+	**GL**	FL	DFLH	BA (S)	
47818	+m	**DS**	DR	XHAC	KM	
47826	+	**WC**	WC	AWCA	CS	
47828	+m	**DS**	DR	XHAC	KM	
47830	+	**GL**	FL	DFLH	BH (S)	
47832	+m	**VN**	DR	XHNB	KM	Solway Princess
47841	+m	**DS**	DR	XHAC	KM	
47843	+m	**RV**	RV	RTLO	CD	VULCAN
47847	+m	**BL**	RV	RTLO	CD (S)	
47848	+m	**RV**	RV	RTLO	CD	TITAN STAR
47851	+	**WC**	WC	AWCA	CS	
47853	+m	**DS**	DR	XHAC	KM	RAIL EXPRESS
47854	+	**WC**	WC	AWCA	CS	Diamond Jubilee

CLASS 50   ENGLISH ELECTRIC   Co-Co

Built: 1967–68 by English Electric at Vulcan Foundry, Newton-le-Willows.
Engine: English Electric 16CVST of 2010 kW (2700 hp) at 850 rpm.
Main Generator: English Electric 840/4B.
Traction Motors: English Electric 538/5A.
Maximum Tractive Effort: 216 kN (48500 lbf).
Continuous Tractive Effort: 147 kN (33000 lbf) at 23.5 mph.
Power At Rail: 1540 kW (2070 hp).   **Train Brakes:** Air & vacuum.
Brake Force: 59 t.   **Dimensions:** 20.88 x 2.78 m.
Weight: 116.9 t.   **Wheel Diameter:** 1092 mm.
Design Speed: 105 mph.   **Maximum Speed:** 90 mph.
Fuel Capacity: 4796 litres.   **RA:** 6.
Train Supply: Electric, index 61.   **Multiple Working:** Orange Square.

Originally numbered D444 & D449.

| 50044 | **B** | 50 | CFOL | KR | Exeter |
| 50049 | **BL** | 50 | CFOL | KR | Defiance |

CLASS 52   BR/MAYBACH   C-C

Built: 1961–64 by BR at Swindon Works.
Engine: Two Maybach MD655 of 1007 kW (1350 hp) at 1500 rpm.
Transmission: Hydraulic. Voith L630rV.
Maximum Tractive Effort: 297 kN (66700 lbf).
Continuous Tractive Effort: 201 kN (45200 lbf) at 14.5 mph.
Power At Rail: 1490 kW (2000 hp).   **Train Brakes:** Air & vacuum.
Brake Force: 83 t.   **Dimensions:** 20.7 m x 2.78 m.
Weight: 110 t.   **Wheel Diameter:** 1092 mm.
Design Speed: 90 mph.   **Maximum Speed:** 90 mph.
Fuel Capacity: 3900 litres.   **RA:** 6.
Train Supply: Steam.   **Multiple Working:** Not equipped.

Never allocated a number in the 1972 number series.

Registered on TOPS as No. 89416.

| D1015 | **M** | DT | MBDL | | TM | WESTERN CHAMPION |

CLASS 55   ENGLISH ELECTRIC   Co-Co

Built: 1961 by English Electric at Vulcan Foundry, Newton-le-Willows.
Engine: Two Napier-Deltic D18-25 of 1230 kW (1650 hp) each at 1500 rpm.
Main Generators: Two English Electric 829/1A.
Traction Motors: English Electric 538/A.
Maximum Tractive Effort: 222 kN (50000 lbf).
Continuous Tractive Effort: 136 kN (30500 lbf) at 32.5 mph.
Power At Rail: 1969 kW (2640 hp).   **Train Brakes:** Air & vacuum.
Brake Force: 51 t.   **Dimensions:** 21.18 x 2.68 m.
Weight: 100 t.   **Wheel Diameter:** 1092 mm.
Design Speed: 105 mph.   **Maximum Speed:** 100 mph.

Fuel Capacity: 3755 litres.   **RA:** 5.
Train Supply: Electric, index 66.   **Multiple Working:** Not equipped.

Originally numbered D9002, D9009 & D9000.

55022 registered on TOPS as No. 89500.

55002	**B**	NM	MBDL	YK	THE KING'S OWN YORKSHIRE LIGHT INFANTRY
55009	**GG**	DP	MBDL	BQ	ALYCIDON
55022	**B**	MW	ELRD	BQ	ROYAL SCOTS GREY

CLASS 56   BRUSH/BR/RUSTON   Co-Co

Built: 1976–84 by Electroputere at Craiova, Romania (as sub contractors for Brush) or BREL at Doncaster or Crewe Works.
Engine: Ruston Paxman 16RK3CT of 2460 kW (3250 hp) at 900 rpm.
Main Alternator: Brush BA1101A.
Traction Motors: Brush TM73-62.
Maximum Tractive Effort: 275 kN (61800 lbf).
Continuous Tractive Effort: 240 kN (53950 lbf) at 16.8 mph.
Power At Rail: 1790 kW (2400 hp).   **Train Brakes:** Air.
Brake Force: 60 t.   **Dimensions:** 19.36 x 2.79 m.
Weight: 126 t.   **Wheel Diameter:** 1143 mm.
Design Speed: 80 mph.   **Maximum Speed:** 80 mph.
Fuel Capacity: 5228 litres.   **RA:** 7.
Train Supply: Not equipped.   **Multiple Working:** Red Diamond.

All equipped with Slow Speed Control.

Non-standard liveries:

56303 All over dark green

56311 Light grey with yellow cabsides.

56007	**FER**	ED	MBDL	BO (S)
56018	**FER**	ZW	MBDL	WH (S)
56031	**FER**	ED	MBDL	BO (S)
56032	**FER**	ED	MBDL	KG (S)
56037	**E**	ED	MBDL	BL (S)
56038	**FER**	ED	MBDL	BO (S)
56051	**FER**	CS	COLS	WH (S)
56060	**FER**	ZW	MBDL	WH (S)
56065	**FER**	ED	MBDL	BO (S)
56069	**FER**	ED	MBDL	BO (S)
56077	**LH**	ED	MBDL	BL (S)
56078	**CS**	CS	COLS	WH (S)
56081	**FER**	ZW	MBDL	BO (S)
56087	**CS**	CS	COFS	WH
56091	**FER**	BA	HTLX	WH
56094	**CS**	CS	COFS	WH
56096	**FER**	EP	EPEX	WH (S)
56098	**BL**	ED	MBDL	BL (S)
56103	**FER**	BA	HTLX	WH (S)

56104	**FER**	ED	MBDL	WH (S)
56105	**CS**	CS	COFS	WH
56106	**FER**	ED	MBDL	BO (S)
56113	**CS**	CS	COFS	WH
56128	**F**	BA	HTLX	WF (S)

56301	(56045)	**FA**	56	HTLX	WH
56302	(56124)	**CS**	ED	COFS	WH
56303	(56125)	**0**	BA	HTLX	WH
56311	(56057)	**0**	BA	HTLX	WH
56312	(56003)	**DC**	BA	HTLX	WH

Jeremiah Dixon Son of County
Durham Surveyor of the
Mason-Dixon Line U.S.A.

CLASS 57   BRUSH/GM   Co-Co

Built: 1964–65 by Brush Traction at Loughborough or BR at Crewe Works as
Class 47. Rebuilt 1997–2004 by Brush Traction at Loughborough.
Engine: General Motors 12 645 E3 of 1860 kW (2500 hp) at 904 rpm.
Main Alternator: Brush BA1101D.
Traction Motors: Brush TM64-68 Mark 1 or Mark 1a.
Maximum Tractive Effort: 244.5 kN (55000 lbf).
Continuous Tractive Effort: 140 kN (31500 lbf) at ?? mph.
Power at Rail: 1507 kW (2025 hp).   **Train Brakes:** Air.
Brake Force: 80 t.   **Dimensions:** 19.38 x 2.79 m.
Weight: 120.6 t.   **Wheel Diameter:** 1143 mm.
Design Speed: 75 mph.   **Maximum Speed:** 75 mph.
Fuel Capacity: 5550 litres.   **RA:** 6
Train Supply: Not equipped.   **Multiple Working:** † DRS system.

Class 57/0. No Train Supply Equipment. Rebuilt 1997–2000.

57001	(47356)		**WC**	WC	AWCA	CS
57002	(47322)	†	**DS**	P	XHCK	KM
57003	(47317)	†	**DS**	P	XHCK	KM
57004	(47347)	†	**DS**	DR	XHCK	KM
57005	(47350)		**AZ**	WC	AWCX	CS (S)
57006	(47187)		**WC**	WC	AWCA	CS
57007	(47332)	†	**DS**	P	XHCK	KM
57008	(47060)	†	**DS**	P	XHCK	KM
57009	(47079)	†	**DS**	P	XHCK	KM
57010	(47231)	†	**DS**	P	XHCK	KM
57011	(47329)	†	**DS**	P	XHCK	KM
57012	(47204)	†	**DS**	P	XHCK	KM

**Class 57/3. Electric Train Supply Equipment. Former Virgin Trains locos.
Rebuilt 2002–04.** Details as Class 57/0 except:

Engine: General Motors 12645F3B of 2050 kW (2750 hp) at 954 rpm.
Main Alternator: Brush BA1101F (recovered from a Class 56) or Brush BA1101G.
Fuel Capacity: 5887 litres.   **Train Supply:** Electric, index 100.
Design Speed: 95 mph.   **Maximum Speed:** 95 mph.
Brake Force: 60 t.   **Weight:** 117 t.

57301	(47845)	i	**Y**	P	QADD	ZG	
57302	(47827)	d	**DS**	P	XHVT	KM	Chad Varah
57303	(47705)	d	**Y**	P	QADD	ZG	
57304	(47807)	d	**DS**	P	XHVT	KM	Pride of Cheshire
57305	(47822)	d	**Y**	P	QADD	ZG	
57306	(47814)	i	**Y**	P	QADD	ZG	
57307	(47225)	d	**DR**	P	XHVT	KM	LADY PENELOPE
57308	(47846)	d	**DS**	P	XHVT	KM	County of Staffordshire
57309	(47806)	d	**DS**	P	XHVT	KM	Pride of Crewe
57310	(47831)	d	**Y**	P	QADD	ZG	
57311	(47817)	d	**DS**	P	XHVT	KM	Thunderbird
57312	(47330)	d	**Y**	P	QADD	ZG	Peter Henderson
57313	(47371)		**AB**	WC	AWCA	CS	
57314	(47372)		**WC**	WC	AWCA	CS	
57315	(47234)		**WC**	WC	AWCA	CS	
57316	(47290)		**AB**	WC	AWCA	CS	

Class 57/6. Electric Train Supply Equipment. Prototype ETS loco. Rebuilt 2001. Details as Class 57/0 except:

Main Alternator: Brush BA1101E.   **Fuel Capacity:** 3273 litres.
Train Supply: Electric, index 95.   **Weight:** 113t.
Design Speed: 95 mph.   **Maximum Speed:** 95 mph.
Brake Force: 60 t.

57601	(47825)	**WC**	WC	AWCA	CS

Class 57/6. Electric Train Supply Equipment. First Great Western locos. Rebuilt 2004. Details as Class 57/3.

57602	(47337)	**FB**	P	EFOO	OO	Restormel Castle
57603	(47349)	**FB**	P	EFOO	OO	Tintagel Castle
57604	(47209)	**GW**	P	EFOO	OO	PENDENNIS CASTLE
57605	(47206)	**FB**	P	EFOO	OO	Totnes Castle

CLASS 58   BREL/RUSTON   Co-Co

Built: 1983–87 by BREL at Doncaster Works.
Engine: Ruston Paxman 12RK3ACT of 2460 kW (3300 hp) at 1000 rpm.
Main Alternator: Brush BA1101B.   **Traction Motors:** Brush TM73-62.
Maximum Tractive Effort: 275 kN (61800 lbf).
Continuous Tractive Effort: 240 kN (53950 lbf) at 17.4 mph.
Power At Rail: 1780 kW (2387 hp).   **Train Brakes:** Air.
Brake Force: 60 t.   **Dimensions:** 19.13 x 2.72 m.
Weight: 130 t.   **Wheel Diameter:** 1120 mm.
Design Speed: 80 mph.   **Maximum Speed:** 80 mph.
Fuel Capacity: 4214 litres.   **RA:** 7.
Train Supply: Not equipped.   **Multiple Working:** Red Diamond.

All equipped with Slow Speed Control.

Class 58s exported for use abroad are listed in section 6 of this book.

58002	**ML**	DB	WNSO	EH (S)
58008	**ML**	DB	WNTS	EH (S)
58012	**F**	DB	WNTS	TO (S)
58017	**F**	DB	WNXX	EH (S)
58022	**F**	DB	WNTS	CD (S)
58023	**ML**	DB	WNTS	TO (S)
58037	**E**	DB	WNXX	EH (S)
58048	**E**	DB	WNTS	CE (S)

CLASS 59   GENERAL MOTORS   Co-Co

Built: 1985 (59001/002/004) or 1989 (59005) by General Motors, La Grange, Illinois, USA or 1990 (59101–104), 1994 (59201) and 1995 (59202–206) by General Motors, London, Ontario, Canada.
Engine: General Motors 16-645E3C two stroke of 2460 kW (3300 hp) at 904 rpm.
Main Alternator: General Motors AR11 MLD-D14A.
Traction Motors: General Motors D77B.
Maximum Tractive Effort: 506 kN (113 550 lbf).
Continuous Tractive Effort: 291 kN (65 300 lbf) at 14.3 mph.
Power At Rail: 1889 kW (2533 hp).   **Train Brakes:** Air.
Brake Force: 69 t.   **Dimensions:** 21.35 x 2.65 m.
Weight: 121 t.   **Wheel Diameter:** 1067 mm.
Design Speed: 60 (* 75) mph.   **Maximum Speed:** 60 (* 75) mph.
Fuel Capacity: 4546 litres.   **RA:** 7.
Train Supply: Not equipped.   **Multiple Working:** AAR System.

Class 59/0. Owned by Aggregate Industries.

59001	**AI**	AI	XYPO	MD	YEOMAN ENDEAVOUR
59002	**FY**	AI	XYPO	MD	ALAN J DAY
59004	**FY**	AI	XYPO	MD	PAUL A HAMMOND
59005	**AI**	AI	XYPO	MD	KENNETH J PAINTER

Class 59/1. Owned by Hanson Quarry Products.

59101	**HA**	HA	XYPA	MD	Village of Whatley
59102	**HA**	HA	XYPA	MD	Village of Chantry
59103	**HA**	HA	XYPA	MD	Village of Mells
59104	**HA**	HA	XYPA	MD	Village of Great Elm

Class 59/2. Owned by DB Schenker.

59201	*	**DB**	DB	WDAK	MD	
59202	*	**DB**	DB	WDAK	MD	
59203	*	**DB**	DB	WDAK	MD	
59204	*	**DB**	DB	WDAK	MD	
59205	*b	**DB**	DB	WDAK	MD	
59206	*b	**DB**	DB	WDAK	MD	John F. Yeoman Rail Pioneer

CLASS 60   BRUSH/MIRRLEES   Co-Co

Built: 1989–93 by Brush Traction at Loughborough.
Engine: Mirrlees 8MB275T of 2310 kW (3100 hp) at 1000 rpm.
Main Alternator: Brush BA1006A.
Traction Motors: Brush TM2161A.
Maximum Tractive Effort: 500 kN (106500 lbf).
Continuous Tractive Effort: 336 kN (71570 lbf) at 17.4 mph.
Power At Rail: 1800 kW (2415 hp).   **Train Brakes:** Air.
Brake Force: 74 (+ 62) t.   **Dimensions:** 21.34 x 2.64 m.
Weight: 129 (+ 131) t.   **Wheel Diameter:** 1118 mm.
Design Speed: 62 mph.   **Maximum Speed:** 60 mph.
Fuel Capacity: 4546 (+ 5225) litres.   **RA:** 8.
Train Supply: Not equipped.   **Multiple Working:** Within class.

DB Schenker Fleet Management Unit: As all operational Class 60s are effectively treated as "common user" by DB Schenker, and allocated to operational pools depending on which duties they are on at the time, all operational locos are shown in the WFMU Fleet Management pool here. Details of the other individual pools can be found in the codes section of this book.

All equipped with Slow Speed Control.

* Refurbished locos.

60034, 60064, 60072, 60073, 60077, 60082, 60084 and 60090 carry their names on one side only.

60500 originally carried the number 60016.

Advertising/promotional liveries:

60074 Teenage Cancer Trust (light blue).
60099 Tata Steel (silver).

60001	*	**DB**	DB	WFMU	TO
60002	+	**E**	DB	WNTS	CD (S) High Peak
60003	+	**E**	DB	WNTS	TO (S) FREIGHT TRANSPORT ASSOCIATION
60004	+	**E**	DB	WNTS	TO (S)
60005	+	**E**	DB	WNTS	TO (S)
60006		**CU**	DB	WNTS	TO (S)
60007	+*	**DB**	DB	WFMU	TO The Spirit of Tom Kendell
60008		**E**	DB	WNTS	TO (S) Sir William McAlpine
60009	+	**E**	DB	WNTS	TO (S)
60010	+*	**DB**	DB	WFMU	TO
60011		**DB**	DB	WFMU	TO
60012	+	**E**	DB	WNTS	TO (S)
60013		**EG**	DB	WNTS	TO (S) Robert Boyle
60014		**EG**	DB	WNTS	TO (S)
60015	+*	**DB**	DB	WFMU	TO
60017	+*	**DB**	DB	WFMU	TO
60018		**E**	DB	WNTS	TO (S)
60019	*	**DB**	DB	WFMU	TO Port of Grimsby & Immingham

60020 +*	DB	DB	WFMU	TO	
60021 +	E	DB	WNTS	TO (S)	
60022 +	E	DB	WNTS	TO (S)	
60023 +	E	DB	WNTS	TO (S)	
60024 *	DB	DB	WFMU	TO	
60025 +	E	DB	WNTS	TO (S)	
60026 +	E	DB	WNTS	TO (S)	
60027 +	E	DB	WNTS	TO (S)	
60028 +	EG	DB	WNTS	CD (S)	John Flamsteed
60029	E	DB	WNTS	CD (S)	Clitheroe Castle
60030 +	E	DB	WNTS	TO (S)	
60031	E	DB	WNTS	TO (S)	
60032	F	DB	WNTS	TO (S)	
60033 +	CU	DB	WNTS	TO (S)	Tees Steel Express
60034	EG	DB	WNTS	TO (S)	Carnedd Llewelyn
60035	E	DB	WFMU	TO	
60036	E	DB	WNTS	TO (S)	GEFCO
60037 +	E	DB	WNTS	TO (S)	
60038 +	E	DB	WNTS	CD (S)	AvestaPolarit
60039 *	DB	DB	WFMU	TO	
60040 *	DB	DB	WFMU	TO	The Territorial Army Centenary
60041 +	E	DB	WNTS	TO (S)	
60042	E	DB	WNTS	TO (S)	
60043	E	DB	WNTS	TO (S)	
60044	ML	DB	WNWX	TO (S)	
60045	E	DB	WFMU	TO	The Permanent Way Institution
60046 +	EG	DB	WNTS	CD (S)	William Wilberforce
60047	E	DB	WNTS	CD (S)	
60048	E	DB	WNTS	TO (S)	
60049	E	DB	WFMU	TO	
60050	E	DB	WNTS	TO (S)	
60051 +	E	DB	WNTS	TO (S)	
60052 +	E	DB	WNTS	TO (S)	Glofa Twr – The last deep mine in Wales – Tower Colliery
60053	E	DB	WNTS	TO (S)	
60054 +*	DB	DB	WFMU	TO	
60055 +	EG	DB	WNTS	CD (S)	Thomas Barnardo
60056 +	EG	DB	WNTS	CD (S)	William Beveridge
60057	EG	DB	WNTS	TO (S)	Adam Smith
60058 +	E	DB	WNTS	TO (S)	
60059 +*	DB	DB	WFMU	TO	Swinden Dalesman
60060	EG	DB	WNTS	TO (S)	
60061	F	DB	WNTS	TO (S)	
60062 *	DB	DB	WFMU	TO	Stainless Pioneer
60063 *	DB	DB	WFMU	TO	
60064 +	EG	DB	WNTS	TO (S)	Back Tor
60065	E	DB	WFMU	TO	Spirit of JAGUAR
60066	EG	DB	WNWX	TO (S)	
60067	EG	DB	WNTS	TO (S)	
60068	EG	DB	WNTS	TO (S)	
60069	E	DB	WNTS	TO (S)	Slioch

60070	+	F	DB	WNTS	TO (S)	John Loudon McAdam
60071	+	E	DB	WFMU	TO	Ribblehead Viaduct
60072		EG	DB	WNTS	TO (S)	Cairn Toul
60073		EG	DB	WNTS	TO (S)	Cairn Gorm
60074	*	AL	DB	WFMU	TO	Teenage Spirit
60075		E	DB	WNTS	TO (S)	
60076		EG	DB	WNTS	CD (S)	
60077	+	EG	DB	WNTS	TO (S)	Canisp
60078		ML	DB	WNTS	TO (S)	
60079	*	DB	DB	WFMU	TO	
60080	+	E	DB	WNTS	TO (S)	
60081	+	GW	DB	WNTS	TO (S)	
60082		EG	DB	WNTS	CD (S)	Mam Tor
60083		E	DB	WNTS	TO (S)	
60084		EG	DB	WNTS	TO (S)	Cross Fell
60085		E	DB	WNTS	TO (S)	MINI Pride of Oxford
60086		EG	DB	WNTS	TO (S)	
60087		E	DB	WNTS	TO (S)	
60088		F	DB	WNTS	TO (S)	
60089	+	E	DB	WNTS	TO (S)	
60090	+	EG	DB	WNTS	TO (S)	Quinag
60091	+*	DB	DB	WFMU	TO	
60092	+*	DB	DB	WFMU	TO	
60093		E	DB	WNTS	TO (S)	
60094		E	DB	WNTS	TO (S)	Rugby Flyer
60095		EG	DB	WNTS	CD (S)	
60096	+	E	DB	WNTS	BZ (S)	
60097	+	E	DB	WNTS	TO (S)	
60098	+	E	DB	WNTS	TO (S)	
60099		AL	DB	WNTS	TO	
60100	*	DB	DB	WFMU	TO	
60500		E	DB	WNTS	TO (S)	

CLASS 66   GENERAL MOTORS/EMD   Co-Co

Built: 1998–2008 by General Motors/EMD, London, Ontario, Canada (Model JT42CWR (low emission locos Model JT42CWRM)) or 2013–14 by EMD/Progress Rail, Muncie, Indiana (66752–759).
Engine: General Motors 12N-710G3B-EC two stroke of 2385 kW (3200 hp) at 904 rpm (low emission locos General Motors 12N-710G3B-T2).
Main Alternator: General Motors AR8/CA6.
Traction Motors: General Motors D43TR.
Maximum Tractive Effort: 409 kN (92000 lbf).
Continuous Tractive Effort: 260 kN (58390 lbf) at 15.9 mph.

Power At Rail: 1850 kW (2480 hp).	**Train Brakes:** Air.
Brake Force: 68 t.	**Dimensions:** 21.35 x 2.64 m.
Weight: 127 t.	**Wheel Diameter:** 1120 mm.
Design Speed: 87.5 mph.	**Maximum Speed:** 75 mph (unless stated).
Fuel Capacity: 6550 litres.	**RA:** 7.
Train Supply: Not equipped.	**Multiple Working:** AAR System.

DB Schenker Fleet Management Unit: As all DB Schenker Class 66s are effectively now treated as "common user" by DB Schenker, and allocated to operational pools depending on which duties they are on at the time, all operational locos are shown in the WFMU Fleet Management pool here. Details of the other individual pools can be found in the codes section of this book.

All equipped with Slow Speed Control.

Class 66s previously used in the UK but now in use abroad are listed in section 6 of this book. Some of the 60 DBS 66s moved to France return to Great Britain from time to time for maintenance or operational requirements.

Advertising livery: 66048 Stobart Rail (two tone blue & white).

Class 66 delivery dates. The Class 66 design has evolved over a 15-year period, with over 400 locomotives delivered. For clarity the delivery dates (by year) for each batch of locos is as follows:

66001–250	EWS (now DB Schenker). 1998–2000 (some now in use in France or Poland)
66301–305	Fastline. 2008. Now used by DRS.
66401–410	DRS. 2003. Now in use with GB Railfreight or Colas Rail and renumbered 66733–737 and 66742–746 (66734 since scrapped).
66411–420	DRS. 2006. Now leased by Freightliner (66411/412/417 exported to Poland).
66421–430	DRS. 2007
66431–434	DRS. 2008
66501–505	Freightliner. 1999
66506–520	Freightliner. 2000
66521–525	Freightliner. 2000 (66521 since scrapped).
66526–531	Freightliner. 2001
66532–537	Freightliner. 2001
66538–543	Freightliner. 2001
66544–553	Freightliner. 2001
66554	Freightliner. 2002†
66555–566	Freightliner. 2002
66567–574	Freightliner. 2003. 66573–574 now used by Colas Rail and renumbered 66846–847.
66575–577	Freightliner. 2004. Now used by Colas Rail and renumbered 66848–850.
66578–581	Freightliner. 2005. Now used by GBRf and renumbered 66738–741.
66582–594	Freightliner. 2007 (66582/583/584/586 exported to Poland).
66595–599	Freightliner. 2008
66601–606	Freightliner. 2000
66607–612	Freightliner. 2002 (66607/609/611/612 exported to Poland)
66613–618	Freightliner. 2003
66619–622	Freightliner. 2005
66623–625	Freightliner. 2007 (66624/625 exported to Poland).
66701–707	GB Railfreight. 2001
66708–712	GB Railfreight. 2002
66713–717	GB Railfreight. 2003

66718–722	GB Railfreight. 2006	
66723–727	GB Railfreight. 2006	
66728–732	GB Railfreight. 2008	
66747–749	Built in 2008 as 20078968-004/006/007 (DE 6313/15/16) for Crossrail AG in the Netherlands but never used. Sold to GB Railfreight in 2012.	
66750–751	Built in 2003 as 20038513-01/04 and have worked in the Netherlands, Germany and Poland. GBRf secured these two locomotives on lease in 2013.	
66752–759	On order for GBRf and due for delivery 2014.	
66951–952	Freightliner. 2004	
66953–957	Freightliner. 2008	

† Replacement for 66521, written off in the Great Heck accident in 2001.

Class 66/0. DB Schenker-operated locos.

All fitted with Swinghead Automatic "Buckeye" Combination Couplers except 66001 and 66002.

† Fitted with additional lights and drawgear for Lickey banking duties.

t Fitted with tripcocks for working over London Underground tracks between Harrow-on-the-Hill and Amersham.

66001 t	**DB**	A	WFMU	TO	
66002	E	A	WFMU	TO	Lafarge Quorn
66003	E	A	WFMU	TO	
66004	E	A	WFMU	TO	
66005	E	A	WFMU	TO	
66006	E	A	WFMU	TO	
66007	E	A	WFMU	TO	
66008	E	A	WFMU	TO	
66009	E	A	WFMU	TO	
66011	E	A	WFMU	TO	
66012	E	A	WFMU	TO	
66013	E	A	WFMU	TO	
66014	E	A	WFMU	TO	
66015	E	A	WFMU	TO	
66016	E	A	WFMU	TO	
66017 t	E	A	WFMU	TO	
66018	E	A	WFMU	TO	
66019 t	E	A	WFMU	TO	
66020	E	A	WFMU	TO	
66021	E	A	WFMU	TO	
66023	E	A	WFMU	TO	
66024	E	A	WFMU	TO	
66025	E	A	WFMU	TO	
66027	E	A	WFMU	TO	
66030	E	A	WFMU	TO	
66031	E	A	WFMU	TO	
66034	E	A	WFMU	TO	
66035	E	A	WFMU	TO	
66037	E	A	WFMU	TO	

66039	E	A	WFMU	TO	
66040	E	A	WFMU	TO	
66041	E	A	WFMU	TO	
66043	E	A	WFMU	TO	
66044	E	A	WFMU	TO	
66046	E	A	WFMU	TO	
66047	E	A	WFMU	TO	
66048	AL	A	WNTS	TO (S)	James the Engine
66050	E	A	WFMU	TO	EWS Energy
66051	E	A	WFMU	TO	
66053	E	A	WFMU	TO	
66054	E	A	WFMU	TO	
66055 †	E	A	WFMU	TO	
66056 †	E	A	WFMU	TO	
66057 †	E	A	WFMU	TO	
66058 †	E	A	WFMU	TO	
66059 †	E	A	WFMU	TO	
66060	E	A	WFMU	TO	
66061	E	A	WFMU	TO	
66063	E	A	WFMU	TO	
66065	E	A	WFMU	TO	
66066	E	A	WFMU	TO	
66067	E	A	WFMU	TO	
66068	E	A	WFMU	TO	
66069	E	A	WFMU	TO	
66070	E	A	WFMU	TO	
66074	E	A	WFMU	TO	
66075	E	A	WFMU	TO	
66076	E	A	WFMU	TO	
66077	E	A	WFMU	TO	Benjamin Gimbert G.C.
66078	E	A	WFMU	TO	
66079	E	A	WFMU	TO	James Nightall G.C.
66080	E	A	WFMU	TO	
66081	E	A	WFMU	TO	
66082	E	A	WFMU	TO	
66083	E	A	WFMU	TO	
66084	E	A	WFMU	TO	
66085	E	A	WFMU	TO	
66086	E	A	WFMU	TO	
66087	E	A	WFMU	TO	
66088	E	A	WFMU	TO	
66089	E	A	WFMU	TO	
66090	E	A	WFMU	TO	
66091	E	A	WFMU	TO	
66092	E	A	WFMU	TO	
66093	E	A	WFMU	TO	
66094	E	A	WFMU	TO	
66095	E	A	WFMU	TO	
66096	E	A	WFMU	TO	
66097	DB	A	WFMU	TO	
66098	E	A	WFMU	TO	

66099	r	E	A	WFMU	TO
66100	r	E	A	WFMU	TO
66101	r	DB	A	WFMU	TO
66102	r	E	A	WFMU	TO
66103	r	E	A	WFMU	TO
66104	r	E	A	WFMU	TO
66105	r	E	A	WFMU	TO
66106	r	E	A	WFMU	TO
66107	r	E	A	WFMU	TO
66108	r	E	A	WFMU	TO
66109		E	A	WFMU	TO
66110	r	E	A	WFMU	TO
66111	r	E	A	WFMU	TO
66112	r	E	A	WFMU	TO
66113	r	E	A	WFMU	TO
66114	r	E	A	WFMU	TO
66115		E	A	WFMU	TO
66116		E	A	WFMU	TO
66117		E	A	WFMU	TO
66118		DB	A	WFMU	TO
66119		E	A	WFMU	TO
66120		E	A	WFMU	TO
66121		E	A	WFMU	TO
66122		E	A	WFMU	TO
66124		E	A	WFMU	TO
66125		E	A	WFMU	TO
66126		E	A	WFMU	TO
66127		E	A	WFMU	TO
66128		E	A	WFMU	TO
66129		E	A	WFMU	TO
66130		E	A	WFMU	TO
66131		E	A	WFMU	TO
66132		E	A	WFMU	TO
66133		E	A	WFMU	TO
66134		E	A	WFMU	TO
66135		E	A	WFMU	TO
66136		E	A	WFMU	TO
66137		E	A	WFMU	TO
66138		E	A	WFMU	TO
66139		E	A	WFMU	TO
66140		E	A	WFMU	TO
66141		E	A	WFMU	TO
66142		E	A	WFMU	TO
66143		E	A	WFMU	TO
66144		E	A	WFMU	TO
66145		E	A	WFMU	TO
66147		E	A	WFMU	TO
66148		E	A	WFMU	TO
66149		E	A	WFMU	TO
66150		E	A	WFMU	TO
66151		E	A	WFMU	TO

66152	**DB**	A	WFMU	TO	Derek Holmes Railway Operator
66154	E	A	WFMU	TO	
66155	E	A	WFMU	TO	
66156	E	A	WFMU	TO	
66158	E	A	WFMU	TO	
66160	E	A	WFMU	TO	
66161	E	A	WFMU	TO	
66162	E	A	WFMU	TO	
66164	E	A	WFMU	TO	
66165	E	A	WFMU	TO	
66167	E	A	WFMU	TO	
66168	E	A	WFMU	TO	
66169	E	A	WFMU	TO	
66170	E	A	WFMU	TO	
66171	E	A	WFMU	TO	
66172	E	A	WFMU	TO	PAUL MELLENEY
66174	E	A	WFMU	TO	
66175	E	A	WFMU	TO	
66176	E	A	WFMU	TO	
66177	E	A	WFMU	TO	
66181	E	A	WFMU	TO	
66182	E	A	WFMU	TO	
66183	E	A	WFMU	TO	
66184	E	A	WFMU	TO	
66185	**DB**	A	WFMU	TO	DP WORLD London Gateway
66186	E	A	WFMU	TO	
66187	E	A	WFMU	TO	
66188	E	A	WFMU	TO	
66192	E	A	WFMU	TO	
66193	E	A	WFMU	TO	
66194	E	A	WFMU	TO	
66197	E	A	WFMU	TO	
66198	E	A	WFMU	TO	
66199	E	A	WFMU	TO	
66200	E	A	WFMU	TO	RAILWAY HERITAGE COMMITTEE
66201	E	A	WFMU	TO	
66204	E	A	WFMU	TO	
66206	E	A	WFMU	TO	
66207	E	A	WFMU	TO	
66213	E	A	WFMU	TO	
66221	E	A	WFMU	TO	
66230	E	A	WFMU	TO	
66232	E	A	WFMU	TO	
66238	E	A	WFMU	TO	
66250	E	A	WFMU	TO	

Class 66/3. Former Fastline-operated loco now operated by DRS. Low emission. Details as Class 66/0 except:

Engine: EMD 12N-710G3B-U2 two stroke of 2420 kW (3245 hp) at 904 rpm.
Traction Motors: General Motors D43TRC.
Fuel Capacity: 5150 litres.

66301	**DS**	BN	XHIM	KM
66302	**DS**	BN	XHIM	KM
66303	**DS**	BN	XHIM	KM
66304	**DS**	BN	XHIM	KM
66305	**DS**	BN	XHIM	KM

66413–434. Low emission. Macquarie Group-owned. Details as Class 66/0 except:

Engine: EMD 12N-710G3B-U2 two stroke of 2420 kW (3245 hp) at 904 rpm.
Traction Motors: General Motors D43TRC.
Fuel Capacity: 5150 litres.

Non-standard livery: 66414 Two tone blue & white (formerly Stobart Rail).

Advertising livery: 66434 Malcolm Rail (blue).

66413	**DS**	MQ	DFHG	LD
66414	**0**	MQ	DFIN	LD
66415	**DS**	MQ	DFTZ	LD
66416	**DS**	MQ	DFIN	LD
66418	**DS**	MQ	DFIN	LD
66419	**DS**	MQ	DFTZ	LD
66420	**DS**	MQ	DFIN	LD
66421	**DS**	MQ	XHIM	KM
66422	**DS**	MQ	XHIM	KM
66423	**DS**	MQ	XHIM	KM
66424	**DS**	MQ	XHIM	KM
66425	**DS**	MQ	XHIM	KM
66426	**DS**	MQ	XHIM	KM
66427	**DS**	MQ	XHIM	KM
66428	**DS**	MQ	XHIM	KM
66429	**DS**	MQ	XHIM	KM
66430	**DS**	MQ	XHIM	KM
66431	**DS**	MQ	XHIM	KM
66432	**DS**	MQ	XHIM	KM
66433	**DS**	MQ	XHIM	KM
66434	**AL**	MQ	XHIM	KM

Class 66/5. Freightliner-operated locos. Details as Class 66/0.

Advertising livery: 66522 Shanks Waste (one half of loco Freightliner green and one half Shanks' Waste light green).

66501	**FL**	P	DFGM	LD	Japan 2001
66502	**FL**	P	DFGM	LD	Basford Hall Centenary 2001
66503	**FL**	P	DFGM	LD	The RAILWAY MAGAZINE
66504	**FH**	P	DFGM	LD	

66505	FL	P	DFGM	LD	
66506	FL	E	DFHH	LD	Crewe Regeneration
66507	FL	E	DFHH	LD	
66508	FL	E	DFRT	LD	
66509	FL	E	DFHH	LD	
66510	FL	E	DFRT	LD	
66511	FL	E	DFRT	LD	
66512	FL	E	DFHH	LD	
66513	FL	E	DFHH	LD	
66514	FL	E	DFRT	LD	
66515	FL	E	DFRT	LD	
66516	FL	E	DFGM	LD	
66517	FL	E	DFGM	LD	
66518	FL	E	DFHH	LD	
66519	FL	E	DFHH	LD	
66520	FL	E	DFRT	LD	
66522	AL	E	DFRT	LD	
66523	FL	E	DFRT	LD	
66524	FL	E	DFHH	LD	
66525	FL	E	DFHH	LD	
66526	FL	P	DFHH	LD	Driver Steve Dunn (George)
66527	FL	P	DFRT	LD	Don Raider
66528	FL	P	DFHH	LD	
66529	FL	P	DFHH	LD	
66530	FL	P	DFHH	LD	
66531	FL	P	DFHH	LD	
66532	FL	P	DFGM	LD	P&O Nedlloyd Atlas
66533	FL	P	DFGM	LD	Hanjin Express/Senator Express
66534	FL	P	DFGM	LD	OOCL Express
66535	FL	P	DFHH	LD	
66536	FL	P	DFHH	LD	
66537	FL	P	DFGM	LD	
66538	FL	E	DFIM	LD	
66539	FL	E	DFHG	LD	
66540	FL	E	DFIM	LD	Ruby
66541	FL	E	DFIM	LD	
66542	FL	E	DFIM	LD	
66543	FL	E	DFIM	LD	
66544	FL	P	DFHG	LD	
66545	FL	P	DFHG	LD	
66546	FL	P	DFHG	LD	
66547	FL	P	DFHG	LD	
66548	FL	P	DFHG	LD	
66549	FL	P	DFHG	LD	
66550	FL	P	DFHG	LD	
66551	FL	P	DFHG	LD	
66552	FL	P	DFHG	LD	Maltby Raider
66553	FL	P	DFHG	LD	
66554	FL	E	DFHG	LD	
66555	FL	E	DFHG	LD	
66556	FL	E	DFIM	LD	

66557	**FL**	E	DFHG	LD	
66558	**FL**	E	DFIM	LD	
66559	**FL**	E	DFHG	LD	
66560	**FL**	E	DFHG	LD	
66561	**FL**	E	DFHG	LD	
66562	**FL**	E	DFIM	LD	
66563	**FL**	E	DFIM	LD	
66564	**FL**	E	DFIM	LD	
66565	**FL**	E	DFIM	LD	
66566	**FL**	E	DFIM	LD	
66567	**FL**	E	DFIM	LD	
66568	**FL**	E	DFIM	LD	
66569	**FL**	E	DFIM	LD	
66570	**FL**	E	DFIM	LD	
66571	**FL**	E	DFIM	LD	
66572	**FL**	E	DFIM	LD	

Class 66/5. Freightliner-operated low emission locos. Details as Class 66/0 except:

Engine: EMD 12N-710G3B-U2 two stroke of 2420 kW (3245 hp) at 904 rpm.
Traction Motors: General Motors D43TRC.
Fuel Capacity: 5150 litres.

66585	**FL**	MQ	DFHG	LD	The Drax Flyer
66587	**FL**	MQ	DFIN	LD	
66588	**FL**	MQ	DFIN	LD	
66589	**FL**	MQ	DFIN	LD	
66590	**FL**	MQ	DFIN	LD	
66591	**FL**	MQ	DFIN	LD	
66592	**FL**	MQ	DFIN	LD	Johnson Stevens Agencies
66593	**FL**	MQ	DFIN	LD	3MG MERSEY MULTIMODAL GATEWAY
66594	**FL**	MQ	DFIN	LD	NYK Spirit of Kyoto
66595	**FL**	BN	DFHG	LD	
66596	**FL**	BN	DFHG	LD	
66597	**FL**	BN	DFHG	LD	Viridor
66598	**FL**	BN	DFHG	LD	
66599	**FL**	BN	DFHG	LD	

Class 66/6. Freightliner-operated locomotives with modified gear ratios.
Details as Class 66/0 except:

Maximum Tractive Effort: 467 kN (105080 lbf).
Continuous Tractive Effort: 296 kN (66630 lbf) at 14.0 mph.
Design Speed: 65 mph.   **Maximum Speed:** 65 mph.

66601	**FL**	P	DFHH	LD	The Hope Valley
66602	**FL**	P	DFHH	LD	
66603	**FL**	P	DFHH	LD	
66604	**FL**	P	DFHH	LD	
66605	**FL**	P	DFHH	LD	
66606	**FL**	P	DFHH	LD	
66607	**FL**	P	DFHG	LD	
66610	**FL**	P	DFHG	LD	

66613	**FL**	E	DFHG	LD	
66614	**FL**	E	DFHG	LD	
66615	**FL**	E	DFHG	LD	
66616	**FL**	E	DFHG	LD	
66617	**FL**	E	DFHG	LD	
66618	**FL**	E	DFHG	LD	Railways Illustrated Annual Photographic Awards Alan Barnes Derek W. Johnson MBE
66619	**FL**	E	DFHG	LD	
66620	**FL**	E	DFHG	LD	
66621	**FL**	E	DFHG	LD	
66622	**FL**	E	DFHG	LD	

Class 66/6. Freightliner-operated low emission loco with modified gear ratios.
Fuel Capacity: 5150 litres.

Advertising livery: 66623 Bardon Aggregates (blue).

66623	**AL**	MQ	DFHG	LD	Bill Bolsover

Class 66/7. GB Railfreight-operated locos. Details as Class 66/0.

Non-standard/Advertising liveries:

66705 **GB** livery but with the addition of "Union Jack" bodyside vinyls.
66709 MSC – blue with images of a container ship.
66720 Day and night (various colours, different on each side).

66701	**GB**	E	GBCM	PG	
66702	**GB**	E	GBCM	PG	Blue Lightning
66703	**GB**	E	GBCM	PG	Doncaster PSB 1981–2002
66704	**GB**	E	GBCM	PG	Colchester Power Signalbox
66705	**GB**	E	GBCM	PG	Golden Jubilee
66706	**GB**	E	GBCM	PG	Nene Valley
66707	**GB**	E	GBCM	PG	Sir Sam Fay GREAT CENTRAL RAILWAY
66708	**GB**	E	GBCM	PG	Jayne
66709	**AL**	E	GBCM	PG	Sorrento
66710	**GB**	E	GBCM	PG	Phil Packer BRIT
66711	**GB**	E	GBCM	PG	
66712	**GB**	E	GBCM	PG	Peterborough Power Signalbox
66713	**GB**	E	GBCM	PG	Forest City
66714	**GB**	E	GBCM	PG	Cromer Lifeboat
66715	**GB**	E	GBCM	PG	VALOUR – IN MEMORY OF ALL RAILWAY EMPLOYEES WHO GAVE THEIR LIVES FOR THEIR COUNTRY
66716	**GB**	E	GBCM	PG	LOCOMOTIVE & CARRIAGE INSTITUTION CENTENARY 1911–2011
66717	**GB**	E	GBCM	PG	Good Old Boy

66718–746. Low emission. GB Railfreight locos. 66733–737 renumbered from former DRS locos 66401–405. 66738–741 renumbered from former Freightliner locos 66578–581. 66742–746 renumbered from former DRS/Colas Rail locos 66406–410/841–845.

All details as Class 66/0 except 66718–732/747–749 as below:

Engine: EMD 12N-710G3B-U2 two stroke of 2420 kW (3245 hp) at 904 rpm.
Traction Motors: General Motors D43TRC.
Fuel Capacity: 5546 litres (66718–722) or 5150 litres (66723–732/747–749).

66747–749 were built for Crossrail AG in the Netherlands but purchased by GBRf in 2012.

66750/751 were built for mainland Europe in 2003, they were leased by GBRf in 2013.

66718	**MT**	E	GBCM	PG	Gwyneth Dunwoody
66719	**MT**	E	GBCM	PG	METRO-LAND
66720	**O**	E	GBCM	PG	
66721	**MT**	E	GBCM	PG	Harry Beck
66722	**MT**	E	GBCM	PG	Sir Edward Watkin
66723	**FS**	E	GBSD	PG	Chinook
66724	**FS**	E	GBSD	PG	Drax Power Station
66725	**FS**	E	GBSD	PG	SUNDERLAND
66726	**FS**	E	GBSD	PG	SHEFFIELD WEDNESDAY
66727	**FS**	E	GBSD	PG	Andrew Scott CBE
66728	**GB**	P	GBCM	PG	Institution of Railway Operators
66729	**GB**	P	GBCM	PG	DERBY COUNTY
66730	**GB**	P	GBCM	PG	Whitemoor
66731	**GB**	P	GBCM	PG	interhub GB
66732	**GB**	P	GBCM	PG	GBRf The First Decade 1999–2009 John Smith – MD
66733 (66401) r	**GB**	P	GBFM	PG	
66735 (66403) r	**GB**	P	GBFM	PG	
66736 (66404) r	**GB**	P	GBFM	PG	WOLVERHAMPTON WANDERERS
66737 (66405) r	**GB**	P	GBFM	PG	Lesia
66738 (66578)	**GB**	GB	GBCM	PG	
66739 (66579)	**GB**	GB	GBCM	PG	Bluebell Railway
66740 (66580)	**GB**	GB	GBCM	PG	
66741 (66581)	**GB**	GB	GBCM	PG	
66742 (66406, 66841)	**GB**	GB	GBRT	PG	ABP Port of Immingham Centenary 1912–2012
66743 (66407, 66842)	**GB**	GB	GBRT	PG	
66744 (66408, 66843)	**GB**	GB	GBRT	PG	Crossrail
66745 (66409, 66844)	**GB**	GB	GBRT	PG	Modern Railways The First 50 Years
66746 (66410, 66845)	**GB**	GB	GBRT	PG	
66747 (20078968-004)	**U**	GB	GBNL	PG	
66748 (20078968-006)	**U**	GB	GBNL	PG	
66749 (20078968-007)	**U**	GB	GBNL	PG	
66750 (20038513-01)		BN	GBDR	LT (S)	
66751 (20038513-04)		BN	GBDR	LT (S)	

66752–759. Low emission. On order for GB Railfreight and due for delivery 2014. Full details awaited.

66752	GB
66753	GB
66754	GB
66755	GB
66756	GB
66757	GB
66758	GB
66759	GB

Class 66/8. Colas Rail locos. Renumbered from former Freightliner locos 66573–577. Details as Class 66/0.

66846 (66573)	**CS**	CS	COLO	RU	
66847 (66574)	**CS**	CS	COLO	RU	
66848 (66575)	**CS**	CS	COLO	RU	
66849 (66576)	**CS**	CS	COLO	RU	Wylam Dilly
66850 (66577)	**CS**	CS	COLO	RU	David Maidment OBE

Class 66/9. Freightliner locos. Low emission "demonstrator" locos. Details as Class 66/0 except:

Engine: EMD 12N-710G3B-U2 two stroke of 2420 kW (3245 hp) at 904 rpm.
Traction Motors: General Motors D43TRC.
Fuel Capacity: 5905/5150 litres.

66951	**FL**	E	DFHG	LD
66952	**FL**	E	DFHG	LD

Class 66/9. Freightliner-operated low emission locos. Owing to the 665xx number range being full further orders of 66/5s are to be numbered from 66953 onwards. Details as Class 66/5 (low emission).

66953	**FL**	BN	DFHG	LD	
66954	**FL**	BN	DFIN	LD	
66955	**FL**	BN	DFIN	LD	
66956	**FL**	BN	DFHG	LD	
66957	**FL**	BN	DFHG	LD	Stephenson Locomotive Society 1909–2009

CLASS 67   ALSTOM/GENERAL MOTORS EMD Bo-Bo

Built: 1999–2000 by Alstom at Valencia, Spain, as sub-contractors for General Motors (General Motors model JT42 HW-HS).
Engine: GM 12N-710G3B-EC two stroke of 2385 kW (3200 hp) at 904 rpm.
Main Alternator: General Motors AR9A/HEP7/CA6C.
Traction Motors: General Motors D43FM.
Maximum Tractive Effort: 141 kN (31770 lbf).
Continuous Tractive Effort: 90 kN (20200 lbf) at 46.5 mph.
Power At Rail: 1860 kW.
Brake Force: 78 t.
Weight: 90 t.
Design Speed: 125 mph.
Train Brakes: Air.
Dimensions: 19.74 x 2.72 m.
Wheel Diameter: 965 mm.
Maximum Speed: 125 mph.

Fuel Capacity: 4927 litres.   **RA:** 8.
Train Supply: Electric, index 66.   **Multiple Working:** AAR System.

All equipped with Slow Speed Control and Swinghead Automatic "Buckeye" Combination Couplers.

67004, 67007, 67009 and 67011 are fitted with cast iron brake blocks for working the Fort William Sleeper. **Maximum Speed:** 80 mph.

67027 carries its name on one side only.

Non-standard liveries:

67026 Diamond Jubilee silver.

67029 All over silver with DB logos.

67001	**AB**	A	WATN	CE	
67002	**AB**	A	WATN	CE	
67003	**AB**	A	WAAN	CE	
67004 r	**E**	A	WABN	CE	Post Haste
67005	**RZ**	A	WAAN	CE	Queen's Messenger
67006	**RZ**	A	WAAN	CE	Royal Sovereign
67007 r	**E**	A	WABN	CE	
67008	**E**	A	WAAN	CE	
67009 r	**E**	A	WABN	CE	
67010	**CM**	A	WAWN	CE	
67011 r	**E**	A	WABN	CE	
67012	**CM**	A	WAWN	CE	A Shropshire Lad
67013	**CM**	A	WAWN	CE	Dyfrbont Pontcysyllte
67014	**CM**	A	WAWN	CE	Thomas Telford
67015	**CM**	A	WAWN	CE	David J. Lloyd
67016	**E**	A	WAAN	CE	
67017	**E**	A	WAWN	CE	Arrow
67018	**DB**	A	WAAN	CE	Keith Heller
67019	**E**	A	WAAN	CE	
67020	**E**	A	WAAN	CE	
67021	**E**	A	WAAN	CE	
67022	**E**	A	WAAN	CE	
67023	**E**	A	WAWN	CE	
67024	**E**	A	WAAN	CE	
67025	**E**	A	WAWN	CE	Western Star
67026	**O**	A	WAAN	CE	Diamond Jubilee
67027	**E**	A	WAAN	CE	Rising Star
67028	**E**	A	WAAN	CE	
67029	**O**	A	WAAN	CE	Royal Diamond
67030 r	**E**	A	WABN	CE	

CLASS 68   VOSSLOH   Bo-Bo

New Vossloh "UKLight" locomotives under construction for DRS, due for delivery 2013–14. Full details awaited.

Built: 2012–13 by Vossloh, Valencia, Spain.
Engine: Caterpillar C175-16 of 2800 kW (3750 hp) at 1740 rpm.
Main Alternator:
Traction Motors:
Maximum Tractive Effort: 317 kN (71 260 lbf).
Continuous Tractive Effort:

Power At Rail:	**Train Brakes:** Air.
Brake Force:	**Dimensions:**
Weight: 85 t.	**Wheel Diameter:**
Design Speed: 100 mph.	**Maximum Speed:** 100 mph.
Fuel Capacity: 6000 litres.	**RA:**
Train Supply:	**Multiple Working:**

68001	BN
68002	BN
68003	BN
68004	BN
68005	BN
68006	BN
68007	BN
68008	BN
68009	BN
68010	BN
68011	BN
68012	BN
68013	BN
68014	BN
68015	BN

CLASS 70   GENERAL ELECTRIC   Co-Co

New GE "PowerHaul" Freightliner locos. An option exists for a further ten locos. 70012 was badly damaged whilst being unloaded in 2011 and was returned to Pennsylvania. 70801 is a Turkish-built Class 70 demonstrator that arrived in Britain in October 2012. It was originally numbered 70099 and is being assessed for use by Colas Rail.

Built: 2009–11 by General Electric, Erie, Pennsylvania, USA or by TÜLOMSAS, Eskişehir, Turkey (70801).
Engine: General Electric PowerHaul P616LDA1 of 2848 kW (3820 hp) at 1500 rpm.
Main Alternator: General Electric GTA series.
Traction Motors: AC-GE 5GEB30.
Maximum Tractive Effort: 544 kN (122 000 lbf).
Continuous Tractive Effort: 427 kN (96 000 lbf) at ?? m.p.h.

Power At Rail:	**Train Brakes:** Air.
Brake Force: 96.7 t.	**Dimensions:** 21.71 x 2.64 m.
Weight: 129 t.	**Wheel Diameter:** 1066 mm.
Design Speed: 75 mph.	**Maximum Speed:** 75 mph.
Fuel Capacity: 6000 litres.	**RA:** 7.
Train Supply: Not equipped.	**Multiple Working:** AAR System.

Non-standard livery: 70801 All over dark green.

70001	**FH**	MQ	DFGI	LD	PowerHaul
70002	**FH**	MQ	DFGH	LD	
70003	**FH**	MQ	DFGH	LD	
70004	**FH**	MQ	DFGH	LD	The Coal Industry Society
70005	**FH**	MQ	DFGH	LD	
70006	**FH**	MQ	DFGH	LD	
70007	**FH**	MQ	DFGI	LD	
70008	**FH**	MQ	DFGI	LD	
70009	**FH**	MQ	DFGI	LD	
70010	**FH**	MQ	DFGH	LD	
70011	**FH**	MQ	DFGH	LD	
70013	**FH**	MQ	DFGH	LD	
70014	**FH**	MQ	DFGH	LD	
70015	**FH**	MQ	DFGH	LD	
70016	**FH**	MQ	DFGH	LD	
70017	**FH**	MQ	DFGI	LD	
70018	**FH**	MQ	DFGI	LD	
70019	**FH**	MQ	DFGI	LD	
70020	**FH**	MQ	DFGI	LD	
70801 (70099)	**0**	GL	MBDL	CF (S)	

2. ELECTRO-DIESEL & ELECTRIC LOCOMOTIVES

CLASS 73   BR/ENGLISH ELECTRIC   Bo-Bo

Electro-diesel locomotives which can operate either from a DC supply or using power from a diesel engine.

Built: 1965–67 by English Electric Co. at Vulcan Foundry, Newton-le-Willows.
Engine: English Electric 4SRKT of 447 kW (600 hp) at 850 rpm.
Main Generator: English Electric 824/5D.
Electric Supply System: 750 V DC from third rail.
Traction Motors: English Electric 546/1B.
Maximum Tractive Effort (Electric): 179 kN (40000 lbf).
Maximum Tractive Effort (Diesel): 160 kN (36000 lbf).
Continuous Rating (Electric): 1060 kW (1420 hp) giving a tractive effort of 35 kN (7800 lbf) at 68 mph.
Continuous Tractive Effort (Diesel): 60 kN (13600 lbf) at 11.5 mph.
Maximum Rail Power (Electric): 2350 kW (3150 hp) at 42 mph.
Train Brakes: Air, vacuum & electro-pneumatic († Air & electro-pneumatic).
Brake Force: 31 t.   **Dimensions:** 16.36 x 2.64 m.
Weight: 77 t.   **Wheel Diameter:** 1016 mm.
Design Speed: 90 mph.   **Maximum Speed:** 90 mph.
Fuel Capacity: 1409 litres.   **RA:** 6.
Train Supply: Electric, index 66 (on electric power only).
Multiple Working: SR 27-way System & Blue Star.

Formerly numbered E6001–E6020/E6022–E6026/E6028–E6049 (not in order).

Locomotives numbered in the 732xx series are classed as 73/2 and were originally dedicated to Gatwick Express services.

Two separate rebuilt projects are underway. For GBRf 73204/209 are being rebuilt at Brush, Loughborough with an MTU R43 4000 V7 1500 hp engine (these will be renumbered 73901/902). For Network Rail 73104/211 are being rebuilt at RVEL, Derby with a pair of QSK19 750 hp engines (these will become 73951–952).

Non-standard liveries:

73107 Two-tone grey.
73109 Mid blue.
73139 Weardale Railway Brown & cream.

73101	**PC**	RE	RVLO	ZA (S)	
73107	**O**	20	MBED	SE	Redhill 1844–1994
73109	**O**	20	MBED	SE	
73119	**B**	GB	GBED	SE	Borough of Eastleigh
73133	**TT**	TT	MBED	BM	
73136	**GB**	GB	GBED	SE	
73138	**Y**	NR	QADD	ZA	

73139	**0**	RE	RVLO	ZA (S)	
73141	**GB**	GB	GBED	SE	Charlotte
73201 †	**B**	20	MBED	SE	Broadlands
73202 †	**GV**	P	MBED	SL	Dave Berry
73205 †	**IC**	GB	GBED	SE	Jeanette
73206 †	**GB**	GB	GBED	SE	Lisa
73207 †	**BL**	GB	GBED	SE	
73208 †	**B**	GB	GBED	SE	
73212 †	**GB**	GB	GBED	SE	Fiona
73213 †	**GB**	GB	GBED	SE	Rhodalyn
73235 †	**SD**	P	HYWD	BM	

The 7390x number series reserved for rebuilt GBRf locomotives:

| 73901 (73209) | | GB | GBBR | LB (S) |
| 73902 (73204) | | GB | GBBR | LB (S) |

The 7395x number series reserved for rebuilt Network Rail locomotives:

| 73951 (73104) | | RE | RVLO | ZA (S) |
| 73952 (73211) | | RE | RVLO | ZA (S) |

CLASS 86   BR/ENGLISH ELECTRIC   Bo-Bo

Built: 1965–66 by English Electric Co at Vulcan Foundry, Newton-le-Willows or by BR at Doncaster Works.
Electric Supply System: 25 kV AC 50 Hz overhead.
Train Brakes: Air.   **Brake Force:** 40 t.
Dimensions: 17.83 x 2.65 m.   **Weight:** 83–86.8 t.
RA: 6.   **Multiple Working:** TDM system.
Train Supply: Electric, index 66.

Formerly numbered E3101–E3200 (not in order).

Class 86s exported for use abroad are listed in section 6 of this book.

Class 86/1. Class 87-type bogies & motors.

Details as above except:
Traction Motors: GEC 412AZ frame mounted.
Maximum Tractive Effort: 258 kN (58000 lbf).
Continuous Rating: 3730 kW (5000 hp) giving a tractive effort of 95 kN (21300 lbf) at 87 mph.
Maximum Rail Power: 5860 kW (7860 hp) at 50.8 mph.
Wheel Diameter: 1150 mm.   **Weight:** 86.8 t.
Design Speed: 110 mph.   **Maximum Speed:** 110 mph.

| 86101 | **B** | EL | ACAC | WN (S) Sir William A Stanier FRS |

Class 86/2. Standard design rebuilt with resilient wheels & Flexicoil suspension.

Traction Motors: AEI 282BZ axle hung.
Maximum Tractive Effort: 207 kN (46500 lbf).
Continuous Rating: 3010 kW (4040 hp) giving a tractive effort of 85 kN (19200 lbf) at 77.5 mph.

Maximum Rail Power: 4550 kW (6100 hp) at 49.5 mph.
Wheel Diameter: 1156 mm.   **Weight:** 85–86.2 t.
Design Speed: 125 mph.   **Maximum Speed:** 100 mph.

Non-standard livery: 86259 BR "Electric blue".

86229		V	EP	EPEX	LM (S)	
86231		V	EP	EPEX	LM (S)	
86234		AR	EP	EPEX	LM (S)	
86235		AR	EP	EPUK	LM (S)	
86246		AR	EP	EPEX	LM (S)	
86247		EX	P	DHLT	CP (S)	
86251		V	EP	EPEX	LM (S)	
86259	x	0	PP	MBEL	WN	Les Ross

Class 86/4.

Traction Motors: AEI 282AZ axle hung.
Maximum Tractive Effort: 258 kN (58000 lbf).
Continuous Rating: 2680 kW (3600 hp) giving a tractive effort of 89 kN (20000 lbf) at 67 mph.
Maximum Rail Power: 4400 kW (5900 hp) at 38 mph.
Wheel Diameter: 1156 mm.   **Weight:** 83–83.9 t.
Design Speed: 100 mph.   **Maximum Speed:** 100 mph.

86401	N	EL	ACXX	WN (S) Northampton Town

Class 86/5. Regeared locomotive operated by Freightliner.

Details as Class 86/4 except:

Continuous Rating: 2680 kW (3600 hp) giving a tractive effort of 117 kN (26300 lbf) at 67 mph.
Maximum Speed: 75 mph.   **Train Supply:** Electric, isolated.

86501 (86608)	FL	FL	DFGC	CP

Class 86/6. Freightliner-operated locomotives.

Details as Class 86/4 except:

Maximum Speed: 75 mph.   **Train Supply:** Electric, isolated.

86604	FL	FL	DFNC	CP
86605	FL	FL	DFNC	CP
86607	FL	FL	DFNC	CP
86609	FL	FL	DFNC	CP
86610	FL	FL	DFNC	CP
86612	FL	P	DFNC	CP
86613	FL	P	DFNC	CP
86614	FL	P	DFNC	CP
86622	FH	P	DFNC	CP
86627	FL	P	DFNC	CP
86628	FL	P	DFNC	CP
86632	FL	P	DFNC	CP
86637	FH	P	DFNC	CP
86638	FL	P	DFNC	CP (S)
86639	FL	P	DFNC	CP

Class 86/7. Europhoenix-owned locomotives. Refurbished Class 86/2s for the UK spot-hire market. Details as Class 86/2 unless stated.

Maximum Speed: 110 mph.   **Weight:** 85t.
Train Supply: Electric, index 74.

86701	(86205)	**CS** EP	EPUK	BH (S)	Orion
86702	(86260)	**EL** EP	EPUK	BH (S)	Cassiopeia

Class 86/9. Network Rail-owned locomotives. Rebuilt from Class 86/2s for use as Mobile Load Bank test locos to test Overhead Line Equipment, initially on the WCML. No. 1 end Traction Motors isolated.

Maximum Speed: 60 mph.   **Train Supply:** Electric, isolated.

86901	(86253)	**Y** NR	QACL	ZA (S)	CHIEF ENGINEER
86902	(86210)	**Y** NR	QACL	ZA (S)	RAIL VEHICLE ENGINEERING

CLASS 87   BREL/GEC   Bo-Bo

Built: 1973–75 by BREL at Crewe Works.
Electric Supply System: 25 kV AC 50 Hz overhead.
Traction Motors: GEC G412AZ frame mounted.
Maximum Tractive Effort: 258 kN (58000 lbf).
Continuous Rating: 3730 kW (5000 hp) giving a tractive effort of 95 kN (21300 lbf) at 87 mph.
Maximum Rail Power: 5860 kW (7860 hp) at 50.8 mph.
Train Brakes: Air.   **Brake Force:** 40 t.
Dimensions: 17.83 x 2.65 m.   **Weight:** 83.3 t.
Wheel Diameter: 1150 mm.   **Design Speed:** 110 mph.
Maximum Speed: 110 mph.   **Train Supply:** Electric, index 95.
RA: 6.   **Multiple Working:** TDM system.

Class 87s exported for use abroad are listed in section 6 of this book.

87002	**B**	EL	ACAC	WN (S) Royal Sovereign

CLASS 88   VOSSLOH   Bo-Bo

Ten new Vossloh bi-mode locomotives on order for DRS and due for delivery 2015. Full details awaited.
Built: 2014–15 by Vossloh, Valencia, Spain.
Electric Supply System: 25 kV AC 50 Hz overhead.
Engine: Caterpillar 12-cylinder 700 kW (940 hp) at 1800 rpm.
Traction Motors: ABB.
Maximum Tractive Effort (Electric):
Maximum Tractive Effort (Diesel):
Continuous Rating: 4000 kW (5360 hp).
Maximum Rail Power: **Dimensions:**
Train Brakes: Air.   **Brake Force:**
Weight: **Wheel Diameter:**
Fuel capacity: **Train Supply:**
Design Speed: 100 mph.   **Maximum Speed:** 100 mph.
RA: **Multiple Working:**

88001	BN
88002	BN
88003	BN
88004	BN
88005	BN
88006	BN
88007	BN
88008	BN
88009	BN
88010	BN

CLASS 90   GEC   Bo-Bo

Built: 1987–90 by BREL at Crewe Works (as sub contractors for GEC).
Electric Supply System: 25 kV AC 50 Hz overhead.
Traction Motors: GEC G412CY frame mounted.
Maximum Tractive Effort: 258 kN (58000 lbf).
Continuous Rating: 3730 kW (5000 hp) giving a tractive effort of 95 kN (21300 lbf) at 87 mph.
Maximum Rail Power: 5860 kW (7860 hp) at 68.3 mph.
Train Brakes: Air.
Brake Force: 40 t.
Weight: 84.5 t.
Design Speed: 110 mph.
Train Supply: Electric, index 95.
Multiple Working: TDM system.

Dimensions: 18.80 x 2.74 m.
Wheel Diameter: 1150 mm.
Maximum Speed: 110 mph.
RA: 7.

90001	b	1	P	IANA	NC
90002	b	1	P	IANA	NC	Eastern Daily Press 1870–2010 SERVING NORFOLK FOR 140 YEARS
90003	b	NX	P	IANA	NC	Rædwald of East Anglia
90004	b	1	P	IANA	NC	City of Chelmsford
90005	b	1	P	IANA	NC	Vice-Admiral Lord Nelson
90006	b	1	P	IANA	NC	Modern Railways Magazine/ Roger Ford
90007	b	1	P	IANA	NC	Sir John Betjeman
90008	b	NX	P	IANA	NC	The East Anglian
90009	b	1	P	IANA	NC	Diamond Jubilee
90010	b	1	P	IANA	NC	BRESSINGHAM STEAM & GARDENS
90011	b	1	P	IANA	NC	Let's Go East of England
90012	b	1	P	IANA	NC	Royal Anglian Regiment
90013	b	1	P	IANA	NC	The Evening Star PRIDE OF IPSWICH 1885–2010 125 YEARS OF SERVING SUFFOLK
90014	b	1	P	IANA	NC	Norfolk and Norwich Festival
90015	b	NX	P	IANA	NC	Colchester Castle
90016	b	FL	P	DFLC	CP	
90017	b	E	DB	WNTS	CE (S)	
90018	b	DB	DB	WEFE	CE	
90019	b	FS	DB	WEFE	CE	

90020 b	E	DB	WEFE	CE	Collingwood
90021	FS	DB	WEFE	CE	
90022	EG	DB	WNTS	CE (S)	Freightconnection
90023	E	DB	WNTS	CE (S)	
90024	FS	DB	WEFE	CE	
90025	F	DB	WNTS	CE (S)	
90026	E	DB	WNTR	CE	
90027	F	DB	WNTS	CE (S)	Allerton T&RS Depot
90028	E	DB	WEFE	CE	
90029	DB	DB	WEFE	CE	
90030	E	DB	WNTS	CE (S)	
90031	E	DB	WNTS	CE (S)	The Railway Children Partnership Working For Street Children Worldwide
90032	E	DB	WNTS	CE (S)	
90033	FE	DB	WNTS	CE (S)	
90034	E	DB	WNWX	CE (S)	
90035	E	DB	WEFE	CE	
90036	DB	DB	WEFE	CE	
90037	E	DB	WNTS	CE (S)	Spirit of Dagenham
90038	FE	DB	WNTS	CE (S)	
90039	E	DB	WEFE	CE	
90040	E	DB	WNTS	CE (S)	The Railway Mission
90041	FL	P	DFLC	CP	
90042	FF	P	DFLC	CP (S)	
90043	FF	P	DFLC	CP	Freightliner Coatbridge
90044	FF	P	DFLC	CP	
90045	FH	P	DFLC	CP	
90046	FL	P	DFLC	CP	
90047	FF	P	DFLC	CP	
90048	FF	P	DFLC	CP	
90049	FH	P	DFLC	CP	
90050	FF	AV	MBEL	CP (S)	

CLASS 91　　　　GEC　　　　Bo-Bo

Built: 1988–91 by BREL at Crewe Works (as sub contractors for GEC).
Electric Supply System: 25 kV AC 50 Hz overhead.
Traction Motors: GEC G426AZ.
Maximum Tractive Effort: 190 kN (43 000 lbf).
Continuous Rating: 4540 kW (6090 hp) giving a tractive effort of 170 kN at 96 mph.
Maximum Rail Power: 4700 kW (6300 hp) at ?? mph.
Train Brakes: Air.
Brake Force: 45 t.
Weight: 84 t.
Design Speed: 140 mph.
Train Supply: Electric, index 95.
Multiple Working: TDM system.
Dimensions: 19.41 x 2.74 m.
Wheel Diameter: 1000 mm.
Maximum Speed: 125 mph.
RA: 7.

Locomotives originally numbered in the 910xx series, but renumbered upon completion of overhauls at Bombardier, Doncaster by the addition of 100 to their original number. The exception to this rule was 91023 which was renumbered 91132.

91114 has been fitted with a second pantograph for evaluation purposes.

Advertising liveries: 91101 Flying Scotsman (purple).

91110 Battle of Britain (black and grey).

91101	**AL**	E	IECA	BN	
91102	**EC**	E	IECA	BN	City of York
91103	**EC**	E	IECA	BN	
91104	**EC**	E	IECA	BN	
91105	**EC**	E	IECA	BN	
91106	**EC**	E	IECA	BN	
91107	**EC**	E	IECA	BN	SKYFALL
91108	**EC**	E	IECA	BN	
91109	**EC**	E	IECA	BN	Sir Bobby Robson
91110	**AL**	E	IECA	BN	BATTLE OF BRITAIN MEMORIAL FLIGHT
91111	**EC**	E	IECA	BN	
91112	**EC**	E	IECA	BN	
91113	**GN**	E	IECA	BN	
91114	**EC**	E	IECA	BN	Durham Cathedral
91115	**EC**	E	IECA	BN	Blaydon Races
91116	**EC**	E	IECA	BN	
91117	**EC**	E	IECA	BN	WEST RIDING LIMITED
91118	**GN**	E	IECA	BN	
91119	**EC**	E	IECA	BN	
91120	**EC**	E	IECA	BN	
91121	**EC**	E	IECA	BN	
91122	**EC**	E	IECA	BN	
91124	**EC**	E	IECA	BN	
91125	**EC**	E	IECA	BN	
91126	**EC**	E	IECA	BN	
91127	**EC**	E	IECA	BN	
91128	**EC**	E	IECA	BN	
91129	**EC**	E	IECA	BN	
91130	**EC**	E	IECA	BN	
91131	**EC**	E	IECA	BN	
91132	**EC**	E	IECA	BN	

CLASS 92   BRUSH   Co-Co

Built: 1993–96 by Brush Traction at Loughborough.
Electric Supply System: 25 kV AC 50 Hz overhead or 750 V DC third rail.
Traction Motors: Asea Brown Boveri design. Model 6FRA 7059B (Asynchronous 3-phase induction motors).
Maximum Tractive Effort: 400 kN (90 000 lbf).
Continuous Rating: 5040 kW (6760 hp) on AC, 4000 kW (5360 hp) on DC.
Maximum Rail Power: **Train Brakes:** Air.
Brake Force: 63 t.   **Dimensions:** 21.34 x 2.67 m.

Weight: 126 t.   **Wheel Diameter:** 1070 mm.
Design Speed: 140 km/h (87 mph).   **Maximum Speed:** 145 km/h (90 mph).
Train Supply: Electric, index 108 (AC), 70 (DC).
RA: 7.

* Modified to operate freight trains on High Speed 1.

Class 92s exported for use abroad are listed in section 6 of this book.

Advertising livery: 92017 Stobart Rail (two-tone blue & white).

92002	**EG**	HB	WTAD	CE	H.G. Wells
92003 *	**EG**	HB	WTHE	CE	Beethoven
92004	**EG**	HB	WNWX	CE (S)	Jane Austen
92005	**EG**	HB	WNWX	CE (S)	Mozart
92006	**EP**	ET	PTXX	CO (S)	Louis Armand
92007	**EG**	HB	WNTR	CE (S)	Schubert
92008	**EG**	HB	WNWX	CE (S)	Jules Verne
92009 *	**DB**	HB	WNTR	CE (S)	Marco Polo
92010	**EP**	ET	GBET	CO	Molière
92011	**EG**	HB	WTAE	CE	Handel
92013	**EG**	HB	WNWX	CE (S)	Puccini
92014	**EP**	ET	PTXX	CO (S)	Emile Zola
92015 *	**DB**	HB	WTHE	CE	
92016 *	**DB**	HB	WTHE	CE	
92017	**AL**	HB	WNTR	CE (S)	Bart the Engine
92018	**EP**	ET	PTXX	CO (S)	Stendhal
92019	**EG**	HB	WNTR	CE (S)	Wagner
92020	**EP**	ET	PTXX	CO (S)	Milton
92021	**EP**	ET	PTXX	CO (S)	Purcell
92022	**EG**	HB	WNTR	CE (S)	Charles Dickens
92023	**EP**	ET	PTXX	CO (S)	Ravel
92024	**EG**	HB	WTAE	CE	J.S. Bach
92026	**EG**	HB	WNTR	CE (S)	Britten
92028	**EP**	ET	GBET	CO	Saint Saëns
92029	**EG**	HB	WTAE	CE	Dante
92030	**EG**	HB	WTAD	CE	Ashford
92031 *	**DB**	HB	WTHE	CE	
92032	**GB**	ET	GBET	CO	IMechE Railway Division
92033	**EP**	ET	PTXX	CO (S)	Berlioz
92035	**EP**	HB	WNWX	CE (S)	Mendelssohn
92036 *	**EG**	HB	WTHE	CE	Bertolt Brecht
92037	**EG**	HB	WTAE	CE	Sullivan
92038	**EP**	ET	GBET	CO	Voltaire
92039	**EG**	HB	WTAE	CE	Johann Strauss
92040	**EP**	ET	PTXX	CO (S)	Goethe
92041	**EG**	HB	WTAE	CE	Vaughan Williams
92042 *	**DB**	HB	WTHE	CE	
92043	**EP**	ET	GBET	CO	Debussy
92044	**EP**	ET	GBET	CO	Couperin
92045	**EP**	ET	PTXX	LB (S)	Chaucer
92046	**EP**	ET	PTXX	LB (S)	Sweelinck

3. EUROTUNNEL LOCOMOTIVES

DIESEL LOCOMOTIVES

0001–0007   MaK   Bo-Bo

Built: 1991–92 by MaK at Kiel, Germany (Model DE1004).
Engine: MTU 12V 396 TC13 of 940 kW (1260 hp) at 1800 rpm.
Main Alternator: ABB.   **Traction Motors:** ABB.
Maximum Tractive Effort: 305 kN (68600 lbf).
Continuous Tractive Effort: 140 kN (31500 lbf) at 20 mph.
Power At Rail: 750 kW (1012 hp).   **Dimensions:** 14.40 x ?? m.
Brake Force: 120 kN.   **Wheel Diameter:** 1000 mm.
Weight: 82 t.   **Maximum Speed:** 100 km/h.
Design Speed: 120 km/h.   **Train Brakes:** Air.
Fuel Capacity: 3500 litres.   **Multiple Working:** Within class.
Train Supply: Not equipped.   **Signalling System:** TVM430 cab signalling.

Note: Registered on TOPS as 21901–907.

0001	**GY**	ET	CO
0002	**GY**	ET	CO
0003	**GY**	ET	CO
0004	**GY**	ET	CO
0005	**GY**	ET	CO

The following two locos were rebuilt from NS 6400 Class 6456 and 6457 (built 1991) and added to the Eurotunnel fleet in 2011.

0006	**GY**	ET	CO
0007	**GY**	ET	CO

0031–0042   HUNSLET/SCHÖMA   0-4-0

Built: 1989–90 by Hunslet Engine Company at Leeds as 900 mm gauge.
Rebuilt: 1993–94 by Schöma in Germany to 1435 mm gauge.
Engine: Deutz FL10L 413FW of 170 kW (230 hp) at 2300 rpm.
Transmission: Mechanical Clark 5000 series.
Maximum Tractive Effort:
Continuous Tractive Effort:
Power At Rail:
Brake Force: **Dimensions:** 6.63 x 2.69 m.
Weight: 26–28 t.   **Wheel Diameter:**
Design Speed: 48 km/h.   **Maximum Speed:** 50 km/h.
Fuel Capacity: **Train Brakes:** Air.
Train Supply: Not equipped.   **Multiple Working:** Not equipped.

Note: * Rebuilt with inspection platforms to check overhead catenary.

0031	**GY**	ET	CO	FRANCES

0032	**GY**	ET	CO	ELISABETH
0033	**GY**	ET	CO	SILKE
0034	**GY**	ET	CO	AMANDA
0035	**GY**	ET	CO	MARY
0036	**GY**	ET	CO	LAURENCE
0037	**GY**	ET	CO	LYDIE
0038	**GY**	ET	CO	JENNY
0039	* **GY**	ET	CO	PACITA
0040	**GY**	ET	CO	JILL
0041	* **GY**	ET	CO	KIM
0042	**GY**	ET	CO	NICOLE

ELECTRIC LOCOMOTIVES

9005–9840   BRUSH/ABB   Bo-Bo-Bo

Built: 1993–2002 by Brush Traction at Loughborough.
Supply System: 25 kV AC 50 Hz overhead.
Traction Motors: Asea Brown Boveri design. Asynchronous 3-phase motors.
Model 6FHA 7059 (as built). Model 6FHA 7059C (7000 kW rated locos).
Maximum Tractive Effort: 400kN (90 000 lbf).
Continuous Rating: Class 9/0 and 9/1: 5760 kW (7725 hp). Class 9/7 and 9/8:
7000 kW (9387 hp).

Maximum Rail Power:	**Multiple Working:** TDM system.
Brake Force: 50 t.	**Dimensions:** 22.01 x 2.97 x 4.20 m.
Weight: 136 t.	**Wheel Diameter:** 1250 mm.
Design Speed: 100 mph.	**Maximum Speed:** 100 mph.
Train Supply: Electric.	**Train Brakes:** Air.

Class 9/0 Original build locos. Built 1993–94.

9005	**EB**	ET	CO	JESSYE NORMAN
9007	**EB**	ET	CO	DAME JOAN SUTHERLAND
9011	**EB**	ET	CO	JOSÉ VAN DAM
9013	**EB**	ET	CO	MARIA CALLAS
9015	**EB**	ET	CO	LÖTSCHBERG 1913
9018	**EB**	ET	CO	WILHELMENIA FERNANDEZ
9022	**EB**	ET	CO	DAME JANET BAKER
9024	**EB**	ET	CO	GOTTHARD 1882
9026	**EB**	ET	CO	FURKATUNNEL 1982
9029	**EB**	ET	CO	THOMAS ALLEN
9033	**EB**	ET	CO	MONTSERRAT CABALLE
9036	**EB**	ET	CO	ALAIN FONDARY
9037	**EB**	ET	CO	GABRIEL BACQUIER

Class 9/7. Increased power freight shuttle locos. Built 2001–02 (9711–23
built 1998–2001 as 9101–13 and rebuilt as 9711–23 2010–12).

9701	**EB**	ET	CO
9702	**EB**	ET	CO
9703	**EB**	ET	CO

9704	**EB**	ET	CO
9705	**EB**	ET	CO
9706	**EB**	ET	CO
9707	**EB**	ET	CO

9711	(9101)	**EB**	ET	CO
9712	(9102)	**EB**	ET	CO
9713	(9103)	**EB**	ET	CO
9714	(9104)	**EB**	ET	CO
9715	(9105)	**EB**	ET	CO
9716	(9106)	**EB**	ET	CO
9717	(9107)	**EB**	ET	CO
9718	(9108)	**EB**	ET	CO
9719	(9109)	**EB**	ET	CO
9720	(9110)	**EB**	ET	CO
9721	(9111)	**EB**	ET	CO
9722	(9112)	**EB**	ET	CO
9723	(9113)	**EB**	ET	CO

Class 9/8 Locos rebuilt from Class 9/0 by adding 800 to the loco number. Uprated to 7000 kW.

9801	**EB**	ET	CO	LESLEY GARRETT
9802	**EB**	ET	CO	STUART BURROWS
9803	**EB**	ET	CO	BENJAMIN LUXON
9804	**EB**	ET	CO	VICTORIA DE LOS ANGELES
9806	**EB**	ET	CO	REGINE CRESPIN
9808	**EB**	ET	CO	ELISABETH SODERSTROM
9809	**EB**	ET	CO	FRANÇOISE POLLET
9810	**EB**	ET	CO	JEAN-PHILIPPE COURTIS
9812	**EB**	ET	CO	LUCIANO PAVAROTTI
9814	**EB**	ET	CO	LUCIA POPP
9816	**EB**	ET	CO	WILLARD WHITE
9817	**EB**	ET	CO (S)	JOSÉ CARRERAS
9819	**EB**	ET	CO	MARIA EWING
9820	**EB**	ET	CO	NICOLAI GHIAROV
9821	**EB**	ET	CO	TERESA BERGANZA
9823	**EB**	ET	CO	DAME ELISABETH LEGGE-SCHWARZKOPF
9825	**EB**	ET	CO	
9827	**EB**	ET	CO	BARBARA HENDRICKS
9828	**EB**	ET	CO	DAME KIRI TE KANAWA
9831	**EB**	ET	CO	
9832	**EB**	ET	CO	RENATA TEBALDI
9834	**EB**	ET	CO	MIRELLA FRENI
9835	**EB**	ET	CO	NICOLAI GEDDA
9838	**EB**	ET	CO	HILDEGARD BEHRENS
9840	**EB**	ET	CO	

▲ First Great Western's four Class 57s are usually only used on the overnight Sleeper trains and opportunities for daylight photos are limited. On 15/07/13 57605 "Totnes Castle" works an 07.55 Penzance–Old Oak Common empty stock at Totnes after the loco had failed the previous night. **David Hunt**

▼ West Coast Railway Company-liveried 57315 leads the 06.05 Sheffield–Bristol Temple Meads Statesman railtour past Isham, south of Kettering on the Midland Main Line, on 04/09/13. **John Coleman**

▲ Two freights were captured heading north on the Midland Main Line on the evening of 19/07/13 – DB Schenker-liveried 60010 works 6E38 13.54 Colnbrook–Lindsey empty bogie tanks as Freightliner 66615 works 6D45 15.53 Luton–Mountsorrel. **Paul Biggs**

▲ Hanson Quarry Products-liveried 59101 "Village of Whatley" works 6C80 Machen Quarry–Westbury Yard stone train at Somerton on 03/08/13. **Jamie Squibbs**

▼ Carrying the new Freightliner PowerHaul livery, 66504 passes Slitting Mill crossing, north of Barrow Hill, with 4E01 03.32 Southampton–Leeds intermodal on 19/08/13. **Andrew Wills**

▲ DBS-liveried 66101 approaches Syston Junction with 4M86 15.51 Ely–Peak Forest empty stone train on 19/07/13. **Joshua Day**

▼ GBRf-liveried 66731 "interhub GB" is seen near Stenson Junction with 6K50 15.12 Toton–Crewe departmental train on 26/08/13. **Paul Biggs**

▲ In the former Wrexham & Shropshire two-tone grey/silver livery now adopted by Chiltern as its Mainline livery, 67012 "A Shropshire Lad" passes Kings Sutton with the 18.15 London Marylebone–Kidderminster on 26/07/13. **Nigel Gibbs**

▼ Freightliner-liveried 70013 passes East Goscote with 6M90 07.00 West Thurrock–Tunstead empty cement tanks on 26/09/13. **Paul Biggs**

▲ Non-standard two-tone grey-liveried 73107 "Redhill 1844–1994" top-and-tails a Cricklewood–Derby test train with 73109 at Cossington on 02/06/13.
Ben Wheeler

▼ Owned by Les Ross, original BR electric blue-liveried 86259 sees regular main line charter work. On 03/08/13 it passes Cromwell (between Retford and Newark) with an 07.18 Edinburgh–London King's Cross private charter. **Lindsay Atkinson**

▲ In a special Battle of Britain livery, East Coast 91110 "Battle of Britain Memorial Flight" crosses Relly Mill Viaduct, just south of Durham, with the 08.00 London King's Cross–Edinburgh on 12/07/13.
Phil Wright

▲ DB Schenker-liveried 90036 passes Hitchin with the diverted southbound ScotRail Highland Sleeper on 17/07/13. **Alisdair Anderson**

▼ DBS Class 92s 92042 and 92016 (dead in train) haul 4O68 03.30 Hams Hall–Dollands Moor intermodal south at Hemel Hempstead on 09/01/13. **Alisdair Anderson**

4. FORMER BR MAIN LINE LOCOS IN INDUSTRIAL SERVICE

Former British Rail main line locomotives considered to be in "industrial use" are listed here. These locomotives do not currently have Network Rail engineering acceptance for operation on the national railway network.

Number Other no./name   Location

Class 03

03084	HELEN-LOUISE	West Coast Railway Company, Carnforth
03179	CLIVE	First Capital Connect, Hornsey Depot, London
03196	JOYCE/GLYNIS	West Coast Railway Company, Carnforth
D2381		West Coast Railway Company, Carnforth

Class 07

D2991	07007	Arlington Fleet Services, Eastleigh Works, Hampshire

Class 08

08202	CHUFFER	The Potter Group, Queen Adelaide, Ely
08308		Hanson Cement, Ketton Cement Works, nr Stamford
08331		Midland Railway-Butterley, Derbyshire
08375	21	Tata Steel, Shotton Works, Deeside, Flintshire
08389		Nemesis Rail, Burton-upon-Trent, Staffordshire
08393		LH Group, Barton-under-Needwood, Staffordshire
08401		Boulby Potash, Boulby Mine, Loftus, North Yorkshire
08411		Colne Valley Railway, Halstead, Essex
08417		RVEL, RTC Business Park, Derby
08418		West Coast Railway Company, Carnforth
08423	H011 14	PD Ports, Teesport, Grangetown, Middlesbrough
08441		Felixstowe Dock & Railway Company, Felixstowe
08442	RICHARD J. WENHAM EASTLEIGH DEPOT	LNWR, Eastleigh Depot, Hampshire
08445		Daventry International Railfreight Terminal, Crick
08447		John G Russell (Transport), Hillington, Glasgow
08460		Colne Valley Railway, Halstead, Essex
08484	CAPTAIN NATHANIEL DARELL	Gloucestershire Warwickshire Railway
08485		West Coast Railway Company, Carnforth
08499		Colas Rail, Canton Depot, Cardiff
08502		Flixborough Wharf, Flixborough, Scunthorpe
08503		Colne Valley Railway, Halstead, Essex
08507		Riviera Trains, Crewe Diesel Depot/Down Holding Sdgs
08511		Felixstowe Dock & Railway Company, Felixstowe
08516		LNWR, Barton Hill Depot, Bristol
08527		Barrow Hill Roundhouse, Chesterfield
08536		RVEL, RTC Business Park, Derby
08568	St. Rollox	Knorr-Bremse Rail Systems, Springburn Depot, Glasgow
08573		Bombardier Transportation, Ilford Works, London

08588		Cemex UK, Washwood Heath, Birmingham
08598	H016 HERCULES	The Potter Group, Queen Adelaide, Ely
08600		AV Dawson, Ayrton Rail Terminal, Middlesbrough
08602	004 BOMBER	Bombardier Transportation, Derby Works
08613	H064	Celtic Energy, Onllwyn Coal & Distribution Centre, West Glamorgan
08622	H028 19	Hanson Cement, Ketton Cement Works, nr Stamford
08629	Wolverton	Knorr-Bremse Rail Systems, Wolverton Works, Milton Keynes
08643		Aggregate Industries, Merehead Rail Terminal
08648	OLD GEOFF 20	PD Ports, Teesport, Grangetown, Middlesbrough
08649	Bradwell	Knorr-Bremse Rail Systems, Wolverton Works, Milton Keynes
08650	ISLE OF GRAIN	Bardon Aggregates, Isle of Grain, Kent
08652		Hanson Aggregates, Whatley Quarry, near Frome
08670		Colas Rail, Canton Depot, Cardiff
08678	ARTILA	West Coast Railway Company, Carnforth
08682	Lionheart	Bombardier Transportation, Derby Works
08683		EMD, Longport Works, Stoke-on-Trent
08685		Barrow Hill Roundhouse, Chesterfield
08697		RVEL, RTC Business Park, Derby
08699		Weardale Railway, Wolsingham, County Durham
08704	D3871	Riviera Trains, Crewe Diesel Depot/Down Holding Sdgs
08730	The Caley	Knorr-Bremse Rail Systems, Springburn Depot, Glasgow
08743	Bryan Turner	SembCorp Utilities Teesside, Wilton, Middlesbrough
08750		Weardale Railway, Wolsingham, County Durham
08756		Tata Steel, Shotton Works, Deeside, Flintshire
08762		Cemex UK, Washwood Heath, Birmingham
08764		Maritime Transport, Tilbury Railport, Tilbury
08765		Nemesis Rail, Burton-upon-Trent, Staffordshire
08774	ARTHUR VERNON DAWSON	AV Dawson, Ayrton Rail Terminal, Middlesbrough
08786		Barrow Hill Roundhouse, Chesterfield, Derbyshire
08787	08296	Hanson Aggregates, Machen Quarry, nr Newport
08807		AV Dawson, Ayrton Rail Terminal, Middlesbrough
08809		Hanson Traction, Washwood Heath, Birmingham
08810		Northern, Heaton Depot, Newcastle
08818	MOLLY	Flixborough Wharf, Flixborough, Scunthorpe
08823	LIBBIE	Daventry International Railfreight Terminal, Crick
08834		Bombardier Transportation, Old Dalby Test Centre, Asfordby
08846	003	Bombardier Transportation, Derby Works
08868		LNWR, Crewe Carriage Depot, Crewe, Cheshire
08870	H024	Weardale Railway, Wolsingham, County Durham
08871	22	PD Ports, Teesport, Grangetown, Middlesbrough
08873		Hams Hall Distribution Park, Coleshill, Warwickshire
08885	H042 18	Weardale Railway, Wolsingham, County Durham
08892		Bombardier Transportation, Derby Works
08903	JOHN W. ANTILL	SembCorp Utilities Teesside, Wilton, Middlesbrough
08905		Hope Construction Materials, Hope Cement Works, Derbyshire
08912		AV Dawson, Ayrton Rail Terminal, Middlesbrough
08913		LH Group, Barton-under-Needwood, Staffordshire
08918		Nemesis Rail, Burton-upon-Trent, Staffordshire
08924	1	Hope Construction Materials, Hope Cement Works, Derbyshire

08933		Aggregate Industries, Merehead Rail Terminal
08936		Tata Steel, Shotton Works, Deeside, Flintshire
08937	D4167	
	BLUEBELL MEL	Bardon Aggregates, Meldon Quarry, near Okehampton
08943		Bombardier Transportation, Central Rivers Depot, Barton-under-Needwood
08947	HOWIE	Arlington Fleet Services, Eastleigh Works, Hampshire
08954		Alstom, Longsight Depot, Manchester
08956		Bombardier Transportation, Old Dalby Test Centre, Asfordby

Class 09

09007	D3671	London Overground, Willesden Depot, London
09014		Nemesis Rail, Burton-upon-Trent, Staffordshire
09022		Victoria Group, Port of Boston, Boston
09204		LNWR, Crewe Carriage Depot, Crewe, Cheshire

Class 14

D9504		Kent & East Sussex Railway
D9529	14029	Nene Valley Railway

Class 20

20056	81	Tata Steel, Appleby-Frodingham Works, Scunthorpe
20066	82	Tata Steel, Appleby-Frodingham Works, Scunthorpe
20168	2 SIR GEORGE EARLE	Hope Construction Materials, Hope Cement Works, Derbyshire
20906	3	Hope Construction Materials, Hope Cement Works, Derbyshire

Class 47

47714		Bombardier Transportation, Old Dalby Test Centre, Asfordby

5. LOCOMOTIVES AWAITING DISPOSAL

Locomotives that are still extant but at scrapyards are listed here.

Class 08

08646	F	European Metal Recycling, Kingsbury
08783	E	European Metal Recycling, Kingsbury
08798	E	European Metal Recycling, Attercliffe
08872	E	European Metal Recycling, Attercliffe
08921	E	European Metal Recycling, Kingsbury

Class 09

09023	E	European Metal Recycling, Kingsbury
09107	E	European Metal Recycling, Kingsbury

Class 37

37415	E	CF Booth, Rotherham

Class 56

56009	O	CF Booth, Rotherham
56049	FER	European Metal Recycling, Kingsbury
56074	FER	European Metal Recycling, Kingsbury
56090	FER	European Metal Recycling, Kingsbury

6. LOCOMOTIVES EXPORTED FOR USE ABROAD

This section details former BR (plus privatisation era) diesel and electric locomotives that have been exported from the UK for use in industrial locations or by a main line operator abroad. Not included are locos that are "preserved" abroad, which are included in our "Preserved Locomotives" publication.

Number Other no./name   Location

Class 04

D2289		Lonato SpA, Lonato Steelworks, Lonato, Brescia, Italy

Class 56

56101	0659 001-5	FLOYD, Hungary
56115	0659 002-3	FLOYD, Hungary
56117	0659 003-1	FLOYD, Hungary

Class 58

58001		Axiom Rail, France, (S) Alizay
58004		Axiom Rail, France, (S) Alizay
58005		Axiom Rail, France, (S) Alizay
58006		Axiom Rail, France, (S) Alizay
58007		Axiom Rail, France, (S) Alizay
58009		Axiom Rail, France, (S) Alizay
58010		Axiom Rail, France, (S) Alizay
58011		Axiom Rail, France, (S) Alizay
58013		Axiom Rail, France, (S) Alizay
58015	L54	Transfesa, Spain, (S) Monforte del Cid, Alicante
58018		Axiom Rail, France, (S) Alizay
58020	L43	Transfesa, Spain, (S) Monforte del Cid, Alicante
58021		Axiom Rail, France, (S) Alizay
58024	L42	Transfesa, Spain, (S) Monforte del Cid, Alicante
58025	L41	DB Schenker, Spain, (S) Albacete
58026		Axiom Rail, France, (S) Alizay
58027	L52	DB Schenker, Spain, (S) Albacete
58029	L44	Transfesa, Spain, (S) Monforte del Cid, Alicante
58030	L46	Transfesa, Spain, (S) Monforte del Cid, Alicante
58031	L45	Transfesa, Spain, (S) Monforte del Cid, Alicante
58032		Axiom Rail, France, (S) Alizay
58033		Axiom Rail, France, (S) Alizay
58034		Axiom Rail, France, (S) Alizay
58035		Axiom Rail, France, (S) Alizay
58036		Axiom Rail, France, (S) Alizay
58038		Axiom Rail, France, (S) Alizay
58039		Axiom Rail, France, (S) Alizay
58040		Axiom Rail, France, (S) Alizay
58041	L36	Transfesa, Spain, (S) Albacete

58042		Axiom Rail, France, (S) Alizay
58043	L37	Transfesa, Spain, (S) Albacete
58044		Axiom Rail, France, (S) Woippy, Metz
58046		Axiom Rail, France, (S) Alizay
58047	L51	Transfesa, Spain, (S) Monforte del Cid, Alicante
58049		Axiom Rail, France, (S) Alizay
58050	L53	DB Schenker, Spain, (S) Albacete

Class 59

59003	YEOMAN HIGHLANDER	
	259 003-2	Heavy Haul Power International, Germany

Class 66

66010	Euro Cargo Rail, France
66022	Euro Cargo Rail, France
66026	Euro Cargo Rail, France
66028	Euro Cargo Rail, France
66029	Euro Cargo Rail, France
66032	Euro Cargo Rail, France
66033	Euro Cargo Rail, France
66036	Euro Cargo Rail, France
66038	Euro Cargo Rail, France
66042	Euro Cargo Rail, France
66045	Euro Cargo Rail, France
66049	Euro Cargo Rail, France
66052	Euro Cargo Rail, France
66062	Euro Cargo Rail, France
66064	Euro Cargo Rail, France
66071	Euro Cargo Rail, France
66072	Euro Cargo Rail, France
66073	Euro Cargo Rail, France
66123	Euro Cargo Rail, France
66146	DB Schenker Rail Polska, Poland
66153	DB Schenker Rail Polska, Poland
66157	DB Schenker Rail Polska, Poland
66159	DB Schenker Rail Polska, Poland
66163	DB Schenker Rail Polska, Poland
66166	DB Schenker Rail Polska, Poland
66173	DB Schenker Rail Polska, Poland
66178	DB Schenker Rail Polska, Poland
66179	Euro Cargo Rail, France
66180	DB Schenker Rail Polska, Poland
66189	DB Schenker Rail Polska, Poland
66190	Euro Cargo Rail, France
66191	Euro Cargo Rail, France
66195	Euro Cargo Rail, France
66196	DB Schenker Rail Polska, Poland
66202	Euro Cargo Rail, France
66203	Euro Cargo Rail, France
66205	Euro Cargo Rail, France
66208	Euro Cargo Rail, France

66209		Euro Cargo Rail, France
66210		Euro Cargo Rail, France
66211		Euro Cargo Rail, France
66212		Euro Cargo Rail, France
66214		Euro Cargo Rail, France
66215		Euro Cargo Rail, France
66216		Euro Cargo Rail, France
66217		Euro Cargo Rail, France
66218		Euro Cargo Rail, France
66219		Euro Cargo Rail, France
66220		DB Schenker Rail Polska, Poland
66222		Euro Cargo Rail, France
66223		Euro Cargo Rail, France
66224		Euro Cargo Rail, France
66225		Euro Cargo Rail, France
66226		Euro Cargo Rail, France
66227		DB Schenker Rail Polska, Poland
66228		Euro Cargo Rail, France
66229		Euro Cargo Rail, France
66231		Euro Cargo Rail, France
66233		Euro Cargo Rail, France
66234		Euro Cargo Rail, France
66235		Euro Cargo Rail, France
66236		Euro Cargo Rail, France
66237		DB Schenker Rail Polska, Poland
66239		Euro Cargo Rail, France
66240		Euro Cargo Rail, France
66241		Euro Cargo Rail, France
66242		Euro Cargo Rail, France
66243		Euro Cargo Rail, France
66244		Euro Cargo Rail, France
66245		Euro Cargo Rail, France
66246		Euro Cargo Rail, France
66247		Euro Cargo Rail, France
66248		DB Schenker Rail Polska, Poland
66249		Euro Cargo Rail, France
66411	66013	Freightliner, Poland
66412	66015	Freightliner, Poland
66417	66014	Freightliner, Poland
66582	66009	Freightliner, Poland
66583	66010	Freightliner, Poland
66584	66011	Freightliner, Poland
66586	66008	Freightliner, Poland
66608	66603	Freightliner, Poland
66609	66604	Freightliner, Poland
66611	66605	Freightliner, Poland
66612	66606	Freightliner, Poland
66624	66602	Freightliner, Poland
66625	66601	Freightliner, Poland

Class 86

86215	91 55 0450 005-8	FLOYD, Hungary
86217	91 55 0450 006-6	FLOYD, Hungary
86218	91 55 0450 004-1	FLOYD, Hungary
86228	91 55 0450 007-4	FLOYD, Hungary
86232	91 55 0450 003-3	FLOYD, Hungary
86233		Bulmarket, Bulgaria (S)
86242	91 55 0450 008-2	FLOYD, Hungary
86248	91 55 0450 001-7	FLOYD, Hungary
86250	91 55 0450 002-5	FLOYD, Hungary
86424	91 55 0450 009-0	FLOYD, Hungary (S)

Class 87

87003	87003-0	BZK, Bulgaria
87004	87004-8 Britannia	BZK, Bulgaria
87006	87006-3	BZK, Bulgaria
87007	87007-1	BZK, Bulgaria
87008	87008-9	BZK, Bulgaria (S)
87009		Bulmarket, Bulgaria
87010	87010-5	BZK, Bulgaria
87012	87012-1	BZK, Bulgaria
87013	87013-9	BZK, Bulgaria
87014	87014-7	BZK, Bulgaria (S)
87017	Iron Duke	Bulmarket, Bulgaria
87019	87019-6	BZK, Bulgaria
87020	87020-4	BZK, Bulgaria
87022	87022-0	BZK, Bulgaria
87023	Velocity	Bulmarket, Bulgaria
87025		Bulmarket, Bulgaria (S)
87026	87026-1	BZK, Bulgaria
87028	87028-7	BZK, Bulgaria
87029	87029-5	BZK, Bulgaria
87033	87033-7	BZK, Bulgaria
87034	87034-5	BZK, Bulgaria

Class 92

92001	Victor Hugo	DB Schenker, Bulgaria
92012	91 53 0472 001-3	
	Mihai Eminescu	DB Schenker, Romania
92025	Oscar Wilde	DB Schenker, Bulgaria
92027	George Eliot	DB Schenker, Bulgaria
92034	Kipling	DB Schenker, Bulgaria

7. CODES

7.1. LIVERY CODES

Livery codes are used to denote the various liveries carried. It is impossible to list every livery variation which currently exists, in particular items ignored for this publication include:

• Minor colour variations.
• Omission of logos.
• All numbering, lettering and brandings.

Descriptions quoted are thus a general guide only. Logos as appropriate for each livery are normally deemed to be carried. The colour of the lower half of the bodyside is stated first.

1	"One" (metallic grey with a broad black bodyside stripe. White National Express/Greater Anglia "interim" stripe as branding).
AB	Arriva Trains Wales/Welsh Government sponsored dark blue.
AI	Aggregate Industries (green, light grey & blue).
AL	Advertising/promotional livery (see class heading for details).
AR	Anglia Railways (turquoise blue with a white stripe).
AZ	Advenza Freight (deep blue with green Advenza brandings).
B	BR blue.
BL	BR Revised blue with yellow cabs, grey roof, large numbers & logo.
CD	Cotswold Rail (silver with blue & red logo).
CE	BR Civil Engineers (yellow & grey with black cab doors & window surrounds).
CM	Chiltern Mainline loco-hauled (two-tone grey & silver with blue stripes).
CS	Colas Rail (yellow, orange & black).
CU	Corus (silver with red logos).
DB	DB Schenker (Deutsche Bahn red with grey roof and solebar).
DC	Devon & Cornwall Railways (metallic silver).
DG	BR Departmental (dark grey with black cab doors & window surrounds).
DR	Direct Rail Services (dark blue with light blue or dark grey roof).
DS	Revised Direct Rail Services (dark blue, light blue & green. "Compass" logo).
E	English Welsh & Scottish Railway (maroon bodyside & roof with a broad gold bodyside band).
EB	Eurotunnel (two-tone grey with a broad blue stripe).
EC	East Coast (silver or grey with a purple stripe).
ECR	Euro Cargo Rail (light grey).
EG	"EWS grey" (as **F** but with large yellow & red EWS logo).
EL	Electric Traction Limited (silver & red).
EP	European Passenger Services (two-tone grey with dark blue roof).
EX	Europhoenix (silver, blue & red).
F	BR Trainload Freight (two-tone grey with black cab doors & window surrounds. Various logos).
FA	Fastline Freight (grey & black with white & orange stripes).
FB	First Group dark blue.
FE	Railfreight Distribution International (two tone-grey with black cab doors & dark blue roof).

FER   Fertis (light grey with a dark grey roof & solebar).
FF   Freightliner grey (two-tone grey with black cab doors & window surrounds. Freightliner logo).
FH   Revised Freightliner {PowerHaul} (dark green with yellow ends & a grey stripe/buffer beam).
FL   Freightliner (dark green with yellow cabs).
FO   BR Railfreight (grey bodysides, yellow cabs & red lower bodyside stripe, large BR logo).
FR   Fragonset Railways (black with silver roof & a red bodyside band lined out in white).
FS   First Group (indigo blue with pink & white stripes).
FY   Foster Yeoman (blue & silver. Cast numberplates).
G   BR Green (plain green, with white stripe on main line locomotives).
GB   GB Railfreight (blue with orange cantrail & solebar stripes, orange cabs).
GC   Grand Central (all over black with an orange stripe).
GG   BR green (two-tone green).
GIF GIF (Spain) light blue with a dark blue band.
GL   First Great Western locomotives (green with a gold stripe (no gold stripe on shunters)).
GN   Great North Eastern Railway {modified} (dark blue with white National Express "interim" stripe as branding).
GV   Gatwick Express EMU (red, white & indigo blue with mauve & blue doors).
GW   Great Western Railway (green, lined out in black & orange).
GY   Eurotunnel (grey & yellow).
HA   Hanson Quarry Products (dark blue/silver with oxide red roof).
HN   Harry Needle Railroad Company (orange with a black roof and solebar).
IC   BR InterCity (dark grey/white/red/white).
K   Black.
LH   BR Loadhaul (black with orange cabsides).
LM   London Midland (white/grey & green with broad black stripe around windows).
M   BR maroon.
MA   Maintrain/East Midlands Trains blue.
ML   BR Mainline Freight (aircraft blue with a silver stripe).
MT   GB Railfreight Metronet (blue with orange cabsides).
N   BR Network SouthEast (white & blue with red lower bodyside stripe, grey solebar & cab ends).
NX   National Express (white with grey ends).
O   Non-standard (see class heading for details).
PC   Pullman Car Company (umber & cream with gold lettering lined out in gold).
RG   BR Parcels (dark grey & red).
RP   Royal Train (claret, lined out in red & black).
RS   RMS Locotec blue.
RV   Riviera Trains (Oxford blue).
RX   Rail Express Systems (dark grey & red with or without blue markings).
RZ   Royal Train revised (plain claret, no lining).
SD   South West Trains outer suburban {Class 450 style} (deep blue, orange & red).
SL   Silverlink (indigo blue with white stripe, green lower body & yellow doors).
ST   Stagecoach (blue with red cabs).
TT   Transmart Trains (all over green).
U   White or grey undercoat.

V	Virgin Trains (red with black doors extending into bodysides, three white lower bodyside stripes).
VN	Northern Belle (crimson lake & cream lined out in gold).
VP	Virgin Trains shunters (black with a large black & white chequered flag on the bodyside).
WA	Wabtec Rail (black).
WC	West Coast Railway Company maroon.
XC	CrossCountry (two-tone silver with deep crimson ends and pink doors).
Y	Network Rail yellow.

7.2. OWNER CODES

Locomotives and rolling stock are owned by various companies and private owners and are allotted codes as follows:

20	Class 20189
40	Class 40 Preservation Society
47	Stratford 47 Group
50	Class 50 Alliance
56	Class 56 Locomotives
70	7029 Clun Castle
71	71A Locomotives
2L	Class 20 Locomotive Society
A	Angel Trains
AI	Aggregate Industries
AM	Alstom
AV	Arriva UK Trains
BA	British American Railway Services
BN	Beacon Rail Leasing
CS	Colas Rail
DB	DB Schenker Rail (UK)
DP	Deltic Preservation Society
DR	Direct Rail Services
DT	The Diesel Traction Group
E	Eversholt Rail (UK)
ED	Edward Stevenson
EL	Electric Traction Limited
EM	East Midlands Trains
EP	Europhoenix
ET	Eurotunnel
EU	Eurostar (UK)
FG	First Group
FL	Freightliner
FW	First Great Western (assets of the Greater Western franchise)
GB	GB Railfreight
GL	GE Capital
HA	The Hanson Group
HB	HBOS plc
HJ	Howard Johnston
HN	Harry Needle Railroad Company

IR	Riley & Son (Railways)
LM	London Midland
MQ	Macquarie Group
MW	Martin Walker
NM	National Museum of Science & Industry
NR	Network Rail
NS	Nemesis Rail
NY	North Yorkshire Moors Railway Enterprises
P	Porterbrook Leasing Company
PO	Other owner
PP	Peter Pan Locomotive Company
RE	Railway Vehicle Engineering
RL	Rail Management Services (trading as RMS Locotec)
RV	Riviera Trains
SN	Southern
TT	Transmart Trains
WA	Wabtec Rail Group
WC	West Coast Railway Company
ZW	Zweig

7.3. LOCOMOTIVE POOL CODES

Locomotives are split into operational groups ("pools") for diagramming and maintenance purposes. The official codes used to denote these pools are shown in this publication.

ACAC	Electric Traction Limited locomotives
ACXX	Electric Traction Limited locomotives for static depot use.
ATLO	Alstom Class 08.
AWCA	West Coast Railway Company operational locomotives.
AWCX	West Coast Railway Company stored locomotives.
CFOL	Class 50 Operations locomotives.
COFS	Colas Rail Class 56.
COLO	Colas Rail Class 47 and 66.
COLS	Colas Rail stored locomotives.
DFGC	Freightliner Intermodal Class 86/5.
DFGH	Freightliner Heavy Haul Class 70.
DFGI	Freightliner Intermodal Class 70.
DFGM	Freightliner Intermodal Class 66.
DFHG	Freightliner Heavy Haul modified Class 66.
DFHH	Freightliner Heavy Haul Class 66.
DFIM	Freightliner Intermodal modified Class 66.
DFIN	Freightliner Intermodal Class 66 (low emission).
DFLC	Freightliner Intermodal Class 90.
DFLH	Freightliner Heavy Haul Class 47.
DFLS	Freightliner Class 08.
DFNC	Freightliner Intermodal Class 86/6.
DFRT	Freightliner Heavy Haul Class 66. Infrastructure services.
DFTZ	Freightliner Heavy Haul locomotives (holding pool).
DHLT	Freightliner locomotives awaiting maintenance/repair/disposal.
EFOO	First Great Western Class 57.

EFPC	First Great Western Class 43.
EFSH	First Great Western Class 08.
EHPC	CrossCountry Class 43.
EJLO	London Midland Class 08.
ELRD	East Lancashire Railway-based main line registered locomotives.
EMPC	East Midlands Trains Class 43.
EMSL	East Midlands Trains Class 08.
EPEX	Europhoenix locomotives for export.
EPUK	Europhoenix UK locomotives.
GBBR	GB Railfreight Class 73/9.
GBCM	GB Railfreight Class 66. General.
GBDR	GB Railfreight Class 66. Locomotives from Germany.
GBED	GB Railfreight Class 73.
GBEE	GB Railfreight Class 20. On hire from Harry Needle/Class 20189.
GBET	GB Railfreight Class 92.
GBFM	GB Railfreight Class 66. RETB fitted.
GBNL	GB Railfreight Class 66. Locomotives from the Netherlands.
GBRT	GB Railfreight Class 66. Network Rail duties.
GBSD	GB Railfreight Class 66.
GBWM	GB Railfreight Class 08/09.
GCHP	Grand Central Class 43.
GPSS	Eurostar (UK) Class 08.
HBSH	Wabtec hire shunting locomotives.
HNRL	Harry Needle Railroad Company hire locomotives.
HNRS	Harry Needle Railroad Company stored locomotives.
HTLX	British American Railway Services locomotives.
HWSU	Southern Class 09.
HYWD	South West Trains Class 73.
IANA	Greater Anglia Class 90.
IECA	East Coast Class 91.
IECP	East Coast Class 43.
MBDL	Non TOC-owned diesel locomotives.
MBED	Non TOC-owned electro-diesel locomotives.
MBEL	Non TOC-owned electric locomotives.
MRSO	RMS Locotec Class 08.
NRLO	Nemesis Rail locomotives.
PTXX	GB Railfreight Class 92 (stored).
QACL	Network Rail Class 86.
QADD	Network Rail diesel locomotives.
QCAR	Network Rail New Measurement Train Class 43.
QETS	Network Rail Class 37.
RFSH	Wabtec Rail locomotives.
RTLO	Riviera Trains Class 47.
RVLO	Rail Vehicle Engineering locomotives.
WAAN	DB Schenker Class 67.
WABN	DB Schenker Class 67. RETB fitted.
WATN	DB Schenker Class 67 for hire to Arriva Trains Wales.
WAWN	DB Schenker Class 67 for hire to Chiltern Railways.
WBAI	DB Schenker Industrial Class 66.
WBAL	DB Schenker Logistics Class 66.
WBAK	DB Schenker Construction Class 66.

WBBI	DB Schenker Industrial Class 66. RETB fitted.
WBBL	DB Schenker Logistics Class 66. RETB fitted.
WBBK	DB Schenker Construction Class 66. RETB fitted.
WBLI	DB Schenker Industrial Class 66. Dedicated locomotives for Lickey Incline banking duties.
WCAI	DB Schenker Industrial Class 60.
WCAK	DB Schenker Construction Class 60.
WCBI	DB Schenker Industrial Class 60. Extended-range fuel tanks.
WCBK	DB Schenker Construction Class 60. Extended-range fuel tanks.
WDAK	DB Schenker Construction Class 59.
WEFE	DB Schenker Class 90.
WFMU	DB Schenker Fleet Management Unit locomotives.
WNSO	DB Schenker locomotives sold awaiting collection.
WNTR	DB Schenker locomotives – short-term maintenance/tactical reserve.
WNTS	DB Schenker locomotives – tactical reserve unserviceable.
WNWX	DB Schenker locomotives – on heavy repair or for heavy repair.
WNXX	DB Schenker locomotives – stored unserviceable.
WNYX	DB Schenker Class 08/09 tactical reserve.
WSSI	DB Schenker Industrial operational Shunters.
WSSL	DB Schenker Logistics operational Shunters
WSSK	DB Schenker Construction operational Shunters.
WSXX	DB Schenker Shunters – internal/depot use.
WTAD	DB Schenker Class 92 for hire to DRS.
WTAE	DB Schenker Class 92.
WTHE	DB Schenker Class 92 with commissioned TVM430 cab signalling equipment for use on High Speed 1.
XHAC	Direct Rail Services Classes 37/4 and 47.
XHCK	Direct Rail Services Class 57/0.
XHHP	Direct Rail Services locomotives – holding pool.
XHIM	Direct Rail Services locomotives – Intermodal traffic.
XHNB	Direct Rail Services Class 47 for use on the Northern Belle.
XHNC	Direct Rail Services locomotives – nuclear traffic/general.
XHSS	Direct Rail Services stored locomotives.
XHVE	Direct Rail Services Class 68.
XHVT	Direct Rail Services Class 57/3 for hire to Virgin Trains.
XYPA	Mendip Rail Class 59/1.
XYPO	Mendip Rail Class 59/0.

7.4. ALLOCATION & LOCATION CODES

Allocation codes are used in this publication to denote the normal maintenance base ("depots") of each operational locomotive. However, maintenance may be carried out at other locations and also by mobile teams. The designation (S) denotes stored.

Code	Location	Depot Operator
BA	Basford Hall Yard (Crewe)	Freightliner
BH	Barrow Hill (Chesterfield)	Barrow Hill Engine Shed Society
BL*	Shackerstone, Battlefield Line	*Storage location only*
BM	Bournemouth	South West Trains
BN	Bounds Green (London)	East Coast
BO	Burton-upon-Trent	Nemesis Rail

BQ	Bury (Greater Manchester)	East Lancashire Rly/Riley & Son Railways
BZ	St Blazey (Par)	*Storage location only*
CD	Crewe Diesel/Down Holding Sdgs	DB Schenker Rail (UK)/Riviera Trains
CE	Crewe International	DB Schenker Rail (UK)
CF	Cardiff Canton	Arriva Trains Wales/Colas Rail
CO	Coquelles (France)	Eurotunnel
CP	Crewe Carriage	LNWR (part of Arriva)
CR	Crewe Gresty Bridge	Direct Rail Services
CS	Carnforth	West Coast Railway Company
EC	Edinburgh Craigentinny	East Coast
EH	Eastleigh	LNWR (part of Arriva)
HT	Heaton (Newcastle)	Northern
KG*	EMR, Kingsbury	European Metals Recycling
KM	Carlisle Kingmoor	Direct Rail Services
KR	Kidderminster	Severn Valley Railway
LA	Laira (Plymouth)	First Great Western
LB	Loughborough Works	Wabtec Rail
LD	Leeds Midland Road	Freightliner Engineering
LE	Landore (Swansea)	First Great Western
LM	Long Marston (Warwickshire)	Motorail Logistics
MD	Merehead	Mendip Rail
NC	Norwich Crown Point	Greater Anglia
NL	Neville Hill (Leeds)	East Midlands Trains/Northern
NY	Grosmont (North Yorkshire)	North Yorkshire Moors Railway
OO	Old Oak Common HST	First Great Western
PG	Peterborough	GB Railfreight
RU	Rugby	Colas Rail
SE	St Leonards (Hastings)	St Leonards Railway Engineering
SH	Southall (London)	Jeremy Hosking Locomotive Services
SL	Stewarts Lane (London)	Southern/Orient Express Hotels
SK	Swanwick Junction (Derbyshire)	Midland Railway-Butterley
TM	Tyseley Locomotive Works	Birmingham Railway Museum
TO	Toton (Nottinghamshire)	DB Schenker Rail (UK)
WF	Wansford (Cambridgeshire)	Nene Valley Railway
WH*	Washwood Heath (Birmingham)	Boden Rail Engineering
WN	Willesden (London)	London Overground
WO*	Wolsingham, Weardale Railway	British American Railway Services
YK	National Railway Museum (York)	National Museum of Science & Industry
ZA	RTC Business Park (Derby)	Railway Vehicle Engineering
ZB	Doncaster Works	Wabtec Rail
ZC	Crewe Works	Bombardier Transportation UK
ZD	Derby Works	Bombardier Transportation UK
ZG	Eastleigh Works	Arlington Fleet Services
ZH	Springburn Depot (Glasgow)	Knorr-Bremse Rail Systems UK
ZI	Ilford Works	Bombardier Transportation UK
ZJ	Stoke-on-Trent Works	Axiom Rail
ZK	Kilmarnock Works	Wabtec Rail Scotland
ZN	Wolverton Works	Knorr-Bremse Rail Systems UK
ZR	York (Holgate Works)	Network Rail

*= unofficial code.